Narrative

A Short-Term Intervention for Traumatic Stress Disorders
after War, Terror, or Torture

# Narrative Exposure Therapy

## A Short-Term Intervention for Traumatic Stress Disorders after War, Terror, or Torture

Maggie Schauer
Frank Neuner
Thomas Elbert

**Library of Congress Cataloging-in-Publication Data**

is available via the Library of Congress Marc Database under the
LC Control Number 2004114228

**National Library of Canada Cataloguing in Publication Data**

Schauer, Maggie
Narrative exposure therapy: a short-term intervention for traumatic stress disorders after war, terror, or torture / Maggie Schauer, Frank Neuner, Thomas Elbert.

Includes bibliographical references.
ISBN 0-88937-290-X

1. Post-traumatic stress disorder – Treatment. 2. Narrative therapy.
3. Victims of violent crimes – Rehabilitation. I. Neuner, Frank II. Elber, Thomas
III. Title

RC552.P67S33 2004     616.85'210651     C2004-906941-1

PUBLISHING OFFICES
**USA:**      Hogrefe & Huber Publishers, 875 Massachusetts Avenue, 7th Floor, Cambridge, MA 02139
             Phone (866) 823-4726, Fax (617) 354-6875, E-mail info@hhpub.com
**EUROPE:**    Hogrefe & Huber Publishers, Rohnsweg 25, D-37085 Göttingen, Germany,
             Phone +49 551 49609-0, Fax +49 551 49609-88, E-mail hh@hhpub.com

SALES & DISTRIBUTION
**USA:**      Hogrefe & Huber Publishers, Customer Service Department, 30 Amberwood Parkway,
             Ashland, OH 44805,
             Phone (800) 228-3749, Fax (419) 281-6883, E-mail custserv@hhpub.com
**EUROPE:**    Hogrefe & Huber Publishers, Rohnsweg 25, D-37085 Göttingen, Germany,
             Phone +49 551 49609-0, Fax +49 551 49609-88, E-mail hh@hhpub.com

COROORATE OFFICE (USA)
             Hogrefe & Huber Publishers, Inc., 218 Main Street, Suite 485, Kirkland, WA 98033

OTHER OFFICES
**CANADA:**    Hogrefe & Huber Publishers, 1543 Bayview Avenue, Toronto, Ontario M4G 3B5
**SWITZERLAND:** Hogrefe & Huber Publishers, Länggass-Strasse 76, CH-3000 Bern 9

Hogrefe & Huber Publishers
Incorporated and Registered in the State of Washington, USA, and in Göttingen, Lower Saxony, Germany

Printed and bound in the USA
ISBN 0-88937-290-X

# Acknowledgments

This manual was written in cooperation with Elisabeth Schauer, MA, MPH, vivo headquarters, Cupramontana, Italy and edited by Christina Robert, MA, University of Minnesota, Minneapolis, USA.

Many people in scientific institutions and aid organizations alike have contributed to the development of Narrative Exposure Therapy (NET). In particular, we thank the following experts for ongoing stimulating discussions and scientific input:

Morton Beiser, MD, Professor, Center for Addiction and Mental Health/CAMH, University of Toronto, Canada
Margret Bradley, PhD, Professor, NIMH Center for the Study of Emotion and Attention, University of Florida, Gainesville, USA
Claudia Catani, PhD, vivo headquaters, Cupramontana, Italy
Unni Karanukara, MD, PhD, Medical Health Advisor, MSF Amsterdam and vivo, The Netherlands
Peter Lang, PhD, Professor and Director, NIMH Center for the Study of Emotion and Attention, University of Florida, Gainesville, USA
Michael Odenwald, Dipl. Psych., vivo outpatient and research clinic at the University of Konstanz, Germany
P. Lamaro Onyut, PhD, Lecturer, Mbarara University of Science and Technology, Uganda
Brigitte Rockstroh, PhD, Professor and Chair, Dept. of Psychology, University of Konstanz and Centre for Psychiatry, Reichenau, Germany
Walton T. Roth, MD, Professor Dept. of Behavioral Science & Psychiatry, Stanford University and Chief Psychiatrist, VA Medical Center, Palo Alto, CA, USA
Martina Ruf, Dipl. Psych., vivo outpatient and research clinic at the University of Konstanz, Germany
Daya Somasundaram, MD, Professor and Director, Dept. of Psychiatry, University of Jaffna, Sri Lanka

and the whole vivo team (www.vivo.org)

Research was supported by the European Refugee Fund, the Deutsche Forschungsgemeinschaft and the NGO vivo.

## Cover Picture

The cover picture was taken by the therapist Dr. Claudia Catani (vivo Italy) during a therapy with a traumatized Sri Lankan child. The life-line is a creative media used in NET that displays the chronological order of good (flowers) and bad or traumatic events (stones) in a child's (or adult's) biography. Usually in the first session, the child starts working together with the therapist on their individual life-line. It is a very moving moment to finally see one's own life with its personal pattern built of flowers and stones disentangled in front of the survivor (see Figure 12, "The Life-Line Exercise: Flowers & Stones," in Chapter 2.2.7)

# Table of Contents

# Introduction: Voices of Victims

The core of psychological trauma is the alienation from life of a wounded soul. In the moment in which pain and harm is purposefully inflicted by one human being onto another, breach of humanity has occurred. Trauma destroys the human kernel that resides in moments or acts that occur within a social context: communication, speech, autobiographical remembrance, dignity, peace, and freedom. Trauma isolates the survivor, alienates life, and freezes the flow of one's personal biography. In this introduction, we will listen to the voices of survivors of violent acts, torture, terror, and dreadfulness:

> I can't go on with this life ... a dream full of horror has not stopped visiting me, at sometimes frequent, sometimes longer, intervals: I am sitting in a peaceful relaxed environment, apparently without tension or affliction; yet I feel a deep and subtle anguish, the definite sensation of an impending threat. And, in fact, as the dream proceeds, slowly and brutally, each time in a different way, everything collapses and disintegrates around me, the scenery, the walls, the people, while the anguish becomes more intense and more precise. Now everything has changed into chaos; I am alone in the centre of a grey and turbid nothing, and now I know what this thing means, and I also know that I have always known it; I am in the Lager once more, and nothing is true outside the Lager. All the rest was a brief pause, a deception of the senses, a dream ... I have fallen into a rather serious depression. I ask you as a "proper doctor" what should I do? I feel the need for help but I do not know what sort."
>
> Primo Levi, Ausschwitz survivor, in a letter to his friend and doctor David Mendel, February 7, 1987

Trauma subsists through the abnormal coding of memories. Conscious recollection of the past has become impossible, while barely noticeable traces sneak through attentional gates and evoke memories of the traumatic events so vivid and real that fear and horror have become routine. An "as if" reenactment of the past becomes a piece of the present, a composite too terrible to utter aloud. Speechlessness from the terror results.

> ... when I think of this time, fear is rising. In the past, we had to suppress it because of the permanent danger, but today I feel strange, because I only re-

> member fragments. Why is that so? I feel as if a part of me is still hiding. I am staring into the darkness and only now and then something flashes up and lays open, a memory of my previous life."
>
> Ervin Staub; child survivor of the Holocaust
> in Stein (1993)

The horror of the past – alive in the moment – can also take over the body and the mind. Listen to the voice of one woman describing those moments when the memories engulfed her being:

> ... when I remember this body, so close to me, so ugly, so intimate, it is still as if there is a dark, bad, black thing entering me at the height of my stomach. It is a thing with arms, like an animal, like a snake, a winding being that enters me and turns around in me and twists. Uh, it makes me shiver. I know it wants to spread, it aims for my whole body, it wants to completely take over me. It wants me to lose control. It has a bad, dark intention ... there is such despair in me, such utter loss of control, such helplessness. I must hide, I am going far, far away in my mind, I cannot bear this .... I feel like I want to explode, I feel like a bomb inside. Yet I have never told anybody. Who will understand the memory of a small girl now that I am nearly 50 years old? People will think I am crazy ...
>
> Excerpt from a vivo documented NET testimony, during therapy with a 49 year-old female Macedonian survivor of childhood sexual abuse, 2003

Loneliness and social isolation are recurring themes among survivors. Unable to talk about the horrors of the past, unable to even comprehend "this other side, this crazy side" in oneself, the feelings become a part of and seem to control the behavior of this new and altered person. As one woman describes her experiences:

> ... Even now many years later the pictures of this day keep coming back to my mind. I look at normal people, like a teacher or a friend, and suddenly the face of the perpetrator appears. Then I get angry and aggressive and try to hurt the person. I throw things and get violent. Sometimes I find myself sitting in strange places, like on top of the roof crying and I have no idea how I got there. It is as if there are two personalities living inside me. One is smart and kind and normal, the other one is crazy and vio-

*lent. I try so hard to control this other side of me. But I fail. Sometimes I feel tears running down my cheek and I wonder why...I have never told anybody what had happened to me during that day and even my father does not know what goes on in my mind and body when I get out of control. This is why I always feel a distance to everybody around me. People don't understand why I act strange sometimes, and I cannot tell them...when I saw children playing and being happy I had to cry because I thought I could never do something like that again."*

Excerpt from a vivo documented NET testimony during therapy with a 13 year-old Somali child survivor, 2003

From an outsider's perspective, it might seem that "Narration" and "Trauma" are radically opposed, and mutually exclusive, as the people suffering these crimes are in too much pain, incapacitated by their enigmatic memory code, to share their stories. However, these two concepts are intimately connected. The atrocities cannot remain buried forever and eventually the victim will be compelled to speak. It is this dichotomy that creates the foothold for this approach and this work.

*After the war, for ten years I didn't speak, I was not a witness, for ten years ...and I was waiting for ten years, really... I was afraid of language. Oh, I knew for ten years I would do something: I had to tell the story. One day, I visited an old Jew...he sat down in his chair, and I in mine, and he began weeping. I have rarely seen an old man weep like that. I didn't know what to do. We stayed there like that, he weeping and I closed in my own pain. And then, at the end, he simply said, "You know, maybe you should talk about it..." In that year, the tenth year, I began my narrative*

Elie Wiesel (survivor of Auschwitz Concentration Camp and Laureate of the Nobel Peace Prize), Interview, Academy of Achievement, 1996

Speechlessness versus the wish and fear to disclose the events forms the central dialectic of psychological trauma. A naturally-occurring conflict exists between wanting to deny the horrible events and feeling the urge to scream out the extent of the atrocities. Regaining one's dignity as well as finding truth in implicating the perpetrator are both fundamental to one's internal process of healing.

Not feeling understood becomes another major hurdle for some victims. The belief lives within that others will never be able to share their experience. Here is one person's testimony to this:

*... It is not because I cannot explain that you won't understand, it is because you won't understand that I can't explain.*

Elie Wiesel (1996)

If this core dynamic of *"not feeling understood in the incommunicability"* is not recognized, treatment is in vain. Previous approaches to healing and overcoming traumatization have tried to address this problem with different strategies, which may not have recognized these issues. By putting words to the trauma, victims are empowered to overcome their sense of speechlessness and lack of explicit memory.

However, clinical intervention techniques are not sufficient. Trauma has societal and political dimensions as well as talking about the experiences, the terror, the torture, and the abuse do. Victims may feel silenced because of the far-reaching political implications that verbalizing the abuse might have. This extends to mental health professionals as well, who may feel discomfort or overwhelmed while listening to stories that demonstrate a gross violation of human rights.

*The ordinary response to atrocities is to banish them from consciousness. Denial, repression, and dissociation operate on a social as well as an individual level...far too often secrecy prevails, and the story of the traumatic event surfaces not as a verbal narrative but as a symptom. Remembering and telling the truth about terrible events are prerequisites both for the restoration of the social order and for the healing of individual victims.*

J. L. Herman (1992)

It is precisely these sociopolitical aspects of healing that need to be explicitly addressed. Only through an externalization of the feelings, abuse and distrust, will true healing occur. Post-conflict peace and reconciliation hinge both on a willingness of society to open their eyes to the abuse, and on the mental health of the individual. Narrative exposure therapy (NET) serves to address both the health of the individual, as well as society, based on the philosophy that these systems are inherently interrelated.

Given this theoretical foundation, NET works at the level of the individual by encouraging the telling of the trauma story and by reliving the past traumatic sceneries within an imaginative exposure design (see Foa, 1998). The goal is to allow for the modification of the fear network co-constructed by the traumatic event (Lang, 1984; 1993). Thus NET weaves *"hot implicit memories"* into the story unfolded by *"cool de-*

*clarative memories"* (Metcalfe, 1999). In this way, intrusive recollections and fragments are integrated into their original context and a consistent autobiographical narrative develops. Part of the process is similar to that of creating a legal testimony. The logic of this part follows the testimony therapy procedure, as developed by Lira and Weinstein in Chile under the Pinocet regime (Cienfuegos & Monelli, 1983).

As narratives are an integrative part of every culture, NET is a culturally universal short-term intervention for the reduction of traumatic stress symptoms in survivors of organized violence, torture, war, rape, civil trauma, and childhood abuse. NET is a form of exposure that encourages traumatized survivors to tell their detailed life history chronologically to a skilled counselor or psychotherapist who will record it, read it back, and assist the survivor with the task of integrating fragmented traumatic memories into a coherent narrative. Describing personal experiences in detail facilitates an internal visual recollection of, and thus exposure to, traumatic memories. Developed for refugees from diverse backgrounds who live in unsafe conditions, narrative exposure serves not only therapeutic purposes but also social and political agenda. While NET is treating survivors through the narrative process, it is also simultaneously documenting violations of human rights.

Overall, this text was written with the goal of integrating psychological rehabilitation of trauma survivors with issues of human rights and dignity on social, academic, and political levels. This work bridges the gap between science and fieldwork. The manual is primarily aimed at mental health practitioners who work in the field (crisis regions, post-conflict settings) as well as those individuals located at clinics, human rights organizations, public health institutions, and academic settings. At the same time, this manual is also written such that it is available to engaged members of the general public. Since story telling, oral tradition, and verbal expression are concepts shared among all of humankind, NET can be tailored to any culture.

Based on scientific evidence from various disciplines (clinical psychology, neuropsychiatry, neuroscience, public health, and refugee studies), NET has been compiled and successfully field-tested (Neuner et al., 2002, 2004a; Onyut et al., in press). Among others, its applicability and efficacy for survivors of violence has been demonstrated under a variety of conditions such as refugee camps/settlements, national or local emergencies or crises, and in European and American

outpatient clinic settings such as the vivo sites in Germany and Italy.

In sum, the core intention of creating NET has been to form a method of psychological treatment that will simultaneously heal while directly contributing to the fight against torture and persecution. The primary elements are thus threefold: healing of the individual, healing from violence committed against one's ethnic or cultural group, and reconciliation from violence.

> *Look, you must speak.*
> *As poorly as we can express our feelings, our memories, but we must try.*
> *We have to tell the story as best as we can.*
> *In truth, I have learned something:*
> *Silence never helps the victim. It only helps the victimizer ...*
> *If I remain silent, I poison my soul*
> Elie Wiesel (1996)

Throughout this process, witnesses and survivors of severe human rights violations are invited to work through their traumatic memories while narrating and testifying the details. This practice enables the processing of painful emotions and the construction of clear contingencies of dangerous and safe conditions, generally leading to significant emotional recovery. If the survivor agrees, the documents (testimonies) that result from this therapy also can directly be used for prosecution of human rights violations or awareness-raising purposes to counteract societal forgetfulness and denial (personal communication with Dori Laub, child survivor, Clinical Professor of Psychiatry at Yale University and Fortunoff Video Archive for Holocaust Testimonies at Yale). As a result, victims of organized violence are offered the chance to claim justice through documentation. From this, an important step may result. The violence is no longer completely senseless; an element of meaning is given to their terrifying experiences and the healing process.

NET's explicit political orientation and goal, enforcing the UN Declaration of Human Rights, has proven to be a significant asset in many ways. International Criminal Tribunals or courts of law that rely on the validity of the data given by survivors can profit from the completeness of a victim's report. Advocacy activities, carried out on behalf of one's own people, also may be based on testimonial evidence provided by NET.

Based on our own experiences and observations of NET in practice, we have concluded that it is indeed possible that NET has empowering consequences on both individual and societal levels. Striving for appropriate mental health services for trauma victims turns out to be anything but a "luxury," especially in resource-poor, conflict-ridden countries. Many survivors suffering from disorders of extreme stress are unable to perform activities crucial to survival, such as creating viable economic and social living conditions for themselves and their families. Victims may be suffering from intrusions and nightmares, their physical health may be deteriorating, and feelings of worthlessness and suicidal ideations are likely to be increasing. Their lives are often characterized by hopelessness, poverty, and the inability to fulfill their societal roles. After treatment, it has been shown that survivors have been able to return to work, tend to their fields, and re-engage in social and intimate relationships. With this, the process of individual and communal recovery is able to begin. Therefore, trauma treatment is a key link between an individual's mental health and those societal factors such as community and economic development.

> *Healing deep-seated antagonism or changing ideologies of antagonism through various types of interactive conflict resolution procedures can contribute to [reconciliation] ... Members of each group can describe the pain and suffering of their group at the hands of the other ... they can grieve for themselves ... they can begin to grieve for the other as well. Members of each group can acknowledge the role of their own group in harming the other. Mutual acknowledgement of responsibility can lead to mutual forgiving. Healing from trauma, which reduces pain, enables people to live constructive lives, and reduces the likelihood of violence by victims and thus a continuing cycle of violence.*
>
> Ervin Staub in Harvey (1998)

If it is indeed true that remembering and narrating the truth about terrible events are prerequisites for both healing of the individual victim as well as restoration of the social order and perhaps even reconciliation, post-conflict peace, and economic development, (Herman, 1992), then why would we share the "*conspiracy of silence*"? At times it seems that we sometimes use the survivors feelings of incommunicability as an excuse not to hear their horrible stories. Here is one victim's voice that wants to encourage us:

> *The enemy wanted to be the one who speaks, and I felt, I still feel, we must see to it that the victim should be the one who speaks and is heard. Therefore, all my adult life, I always try to listen to the victim ...*
>
> *Be sensitive in every way possible. There is nothing more exciting than to be a sensitive person. Because then you listen ...*
>
> *... Of course it hurts. Sensitivity is painful. Think of those that you have to be sensitive to. Their pain is greater than yours.*
>
> Elie Wiesel (1996)

There are fundamental issues that continue to arise as we conduct this work. For instance: Am I convinced that it is good for the survivor to be exposed again to the traumatic memories? Will it contribute to healing, or cause more pain and disturbance? Do I want to hear these stories? What do I do about the fear I have listening to these stories? Searching for answers, we honor the victims' voice:

> *If you had seen such things that I went through, you'll never forget. Before I had told my story, the horrible experiences felt like wounds in my body that didn't want to heal. I was always sad. I didn't know what could help. The pictures were always there and I was shaking with fear, so I wasn't able to dig in the fields. Because of the pain I couldn't find the words. Only pieces of speech. Then you came and were not afraid to listen to me. To hear all of it. I never thought anybody could bear hearing this. Now I hold the story in my heart and on the paper in my hands. I cannot read, but my children will finally know what has happened, what enables them to fight for peace. Because I went through the pain, I got my past back. Now my heart is free ...*
>
> Excerpt from a vivo documented NET testimony with a 35-year old female survivor of the Sudan Genocide, 2000.

# 2 Theoretical background

## 2.1 Traumatic Stress

### 2.1.1 Traumatic Events

What we call trauma in colloquial language does not correspond well to the definition provided within the fields of clinical psychology and psychiatry. Trauma does not just refer to any breakdown in coping strategies in the face of difficult life events. Trauma means a cut into the soul as a result of a horrifying experience (see also Elbert & Schauer, 2002, for a brief outline of the concept). The wound may persist as a crippling disease with its core conceptualized as post-traumatic stress disorder. The term "trauma" originally comes from the Greek language and means "injury or wound". It was first used in the field of medicine to describe bodily injury, such as with emergency medicine ("physical trauma after an accident") or neurology ("traumatic brain injury"). Later, psychiatrists suggested that extremely stressful, typically life-threatening events could be considered traumatic, as those events could contribute to the onset of mental disorders, even without any physical injury. Trauma thus becomes the "wound of the soul" related to disordered brain functioning. Consequently, the behavior, the self-report of a specific symptom pattern and also means of examining the brain functioning of survivors become tools for "viewing" the mental injury. We will see in the next chapter how those survivors of trauma who still suffer from the impacts of the events also experience severe emotional pain when reminded of the event. Quite naturally, they try hard to avoid such reminders and to suppress related feelings. This is analogous to someone who has had a physical injury and who avoids further pain by not moving or touching the injured part of the body.

Traumatic events are characterized by extraordinary circumstances and by the presence of distinct physiological alarm responses of the victims when they do occur. Traumatic events are not just bad experiences that cause people to suffer. They are noted for the quality of the impact they have on human beings. These oftentimes life-threatening events can have a horrifying impact, regardless of whether the person was directly affected or whether the person simply witnessed the event happening to someone else. Both situations can be equally traumatizing; especially when the event happens to someone close, like a family member or a loved one. We can classify traumatic experiences into two types: man-made disasters and natural disasters. Examples of traumatic events caused by other humans are: exposure to combat, rape, torture, witnessing a massacre or mass killing, being held prisoner of war or experiencing catastrophes such as air-plane crashes or severe car accidents. Natural disasters classified as trauma may include floods, earthquakes, hurricanes, or volcanic eruptions. In contrast, experiences of loss, such as losing a business, or of bereavement, such as caring for an elderly parent, are not considered traumatic. Neither would viewing a horrifying movie or reading a violent book qualify as a *traumatic* experience. Adult observers are constantly aware that movies are not real and therefore do not panic in a state of alarm.

Even extremely stressful events are only considered traumatic when the victim or the eye-witness enter a physiological *alarm state* during the event and the individual feels terrified or helpless or both. In this case, a cascade of responses in the body and mind is triggered which can damage both the mind and the body. The stressful event is then called a traumatic one. This cascade involves a series of very rapid changes in body and brain mediated by hormones and neural activity, which affect all organs and include increased heart rate, muscle tone, blood-flow, and metabolism; digestion is put on halt and resources are withdrawn from the immune system.

| Summary | What is trauma? |
|---|---|
| Psychological "trauma" is the experience and psychological impact of events that are life-threatening or include a danger of injury so severe that the person is horrified, feels helpless, and experiences a psychophysiological alarm response during and shortly following the experience. | |

### 2.1.2 Stress and Allostatic Load

The body, including the brain, has the ability to deal with danger in a flexible and adaptive way. In contrast to homeostasis, i.e., the organism's ability to maintain a steady internal state, allostasis refers to the flexibility in the adjustment to stressors that range from physical deprivation (cold, noise, deprivation of food, sleep, etc.) to the real or imagined fear-provoking situations that trigger an alarm response and may result in disorders of the trauma spectrum. The Greek word "allo," meaning variable, is used by McEwen (2002) to emphasize the ability to choose from an arsenal of attack and defense armaments to counter negative impact. Even upon minor cues the brain can activate any appropriate alternative of the flight-fight-freeze defense cascade. The cascade of responses to stress is directed by three bodily systems (overview Teicher et al., 2002; Mc Ewen, 2002; Elbert & Rockstroh, 2003). The hippocampus, which is primarily responsible for functions associated with the build-up of memory, and the hypothalamic-pituitary-adrenal (HPA) axis is the elite force of the defense cascade and involved in the feedback regulation of cortisol, a stress hormone secreted by the adrenal gland. A second stake involves the amygdale (related to the development and processing of emotions), locus coeruleus, adrenal gland, and sympathetic nervous system, all crucial for directing blood flow, increasing awareness and mobilizing the fight/flight response. A third, less explored axis involves the vasopression-oxytocin peptides. Finally, the immune system is involved in adaptive and maladaptive responses (see Segerstrom & Miller, 2004, for an overview): short-lasting acute and naturalistic stressors are associated with adaptive up-regulation of some, but down-regulation in other parameters of immunity, while chronic stressors lead to immune suppression. All of these systems – when functioning properly – help us to deal with crisis. They are also involved in the stress-protective effect of positive social interaction, while, in turn, a dysregulated metabolism of specific biological systems may be associated with clinical disorders.

When unremitting stress forces the three axes of stress response to tilt in one direction, the result can be anything from a long-lasting head cold to depression. When tilted the other way, towards a flattening of the rhythm of stress hormones, undesirable consequences may be abdominal fat, loss of muscle mass, and mental ailing. When the danger is over, the stress response shuts down – at least in wild animals. Humans, however, seem to be unique in that they can keep the HPA axis going indefinitely. The stress hormones ultimately make their way back to the brain, affecting both behavior and health. Allostasis has evolved as the adequate response for running away from a predator, for escaping acute danger, which may be inappropriate in a modern human. Still, the same physiological responses (like the supply of addi-

tional blood and oxygen to muscles, etc.) may be activated in the face of modern stressful stimuli, which cannot be attacked nor escaped by running away. Prolonged stress will turn (adaptive) allostasis into allostatic load, and the permanent initiation of warding off stress will turn the adaptive physiological responses into maladaptive disease in the form of aches and pains, loss of appetite, or overeating. A long-term high allostatic load will damage organs, including the brain.

Increasing evidence suggests that the brain is affected in various ways by stressful environments and experiences. Two prime targets for stress hormones in the brain are the hippocampus and the amygdala. It is well established that acute elevations of adrenal stress hormones (catecholamines and glucocorticoids) enhance memory consolidation of emotionally arousing, contextual (hippocampus-dependent) information in a dose-dependent manner in animals (Roozendaal et al., 2001) and humans (Cahill et al., 1994; Buchanan et al., 2001). These enhancing effects of stress hormones are mediated by structures within (the basolateral nucleus of) the amygdala (Cahill et al., 1995; McGaugh, 2002). Whereas the support of stress hormones might be adaptive, whenever lasting memories of vital information (e.g., dangerous situations) have to be established, this mechanism may become maladaptive in conditions of extreme stress, when persistent and intrusive memories of a traumatic event promote the development of trauma-related disorders. However, acute elevations of glucocorticoids not only have enhancing effects on memory consolidation, but also impairing effects on memory retrieval (de Quervain et al., 1998, 2000; Roozendaal et al., 2003). Furthermore, chronic glucocorticoid excess can lead to disruption of brain synaptic plasticity, atrophy of dendritic processes, and reduced neuronal ability to survive a variety of coincident insults (Sapolsky, 1999). Moreover, perinatal stress changes the HPA axis, delays cognitive and emotional development, and may impair avoidance learning for the rest of a person's life (Meaney et al., 1988; Bock et al., 2003; Teicher et al., 2002).

Thus, stressful experiences differentially activate a variety of responses designed by evolution to counter danger. The different chemical messengers may cause deficits in hippocampus-based learning and memory, and their effects on the amygdala and the medial prefrontal and cingulated cortex may lead to impaired inhibition of fear responses. As a result, emotional and autobiographic memory may become fragmented (see Section 1.1). In addition, repeated or chronic exposure to traumatic stress may lead to long-term dysregulation of these systems leading to impaired functioning and to symptoms of stress-related disorders such as hyperarousal, dissociation, flashbacks, avoidance, and depression (see Section 1.1.4).

### 2.1.3 Organized Violence

*The Nature of Organized Violence*

This manual deals with the traumatizing consequences of organized violence on mental health. Organized violence includes war, torture, and any other systematic violation of human rights. Organized violence is not a psychological crisis, such as a pervasive or chronic mental health issue like schizophrenia would be. It is important to be aware of the political context of war and torture and to comprehend the meaning of organized violence for individuals and society.

Despite the destructive power of violence, the consequences of this behavior have remained a universal and enduring phenomenon. Human history is often recounted in terms of wars between nations and bloody conflicts in states. Different religions and social movements have tried to condemn violence and proposed a peaceful coexistence of people. Nevertheless, violence continues to preside in many parts of the world and the danger of war and terror remains a continuous and currently even increasing threat for large numbers of people.

Violence appears in different forms. Prominent classifications of violence exist according to their context (Derriennic, 1971). A major dimension for qualifying types of violence rests on the degree of organization. Examples of unorganized types of violence include assaults, domestic violence, sexual abuse, and other violent crimes against individuals. Organized violence includes wars, armed conflict, and political persecution. These provide the context for a more systematic order of organized violence, which include torture, massacres, hand-to-hand combat, and bombardments.

*Survivors of Organized Violence*

An obvious consequence of organized violence is that many people have to flee from their region of origin because of war or persecution. Few war reporters dare to visit the insecure war regions. Consequently, there

are often no photographs and films from combats, atrocities, and torture. Media reports of overcrowded refugee camps are probably the most common source of information about the consequences of organized violence and the displacement of individuals. In 2001, the United Nations High Commissioner for Refugees (UNHCR) counted nearly 40 million people who had fled from their homes with 21 million leaving their home country (UNHCR, 2002b).

No matter where refugees or internally displaced people flee to after war and persecution, most exiles are not safe or accommodating (Karunakara et al., 2004). Many reports indicate that initial receptions by host government authorities and humanitarian agencies are impersonal and threatening, and that refugees assume roles of dependency and helplessness (Doná & Berry, 1999). While developments of social networks, family reunions, and permanent settlements do occur (Castles & Miller, 1993), harsh living conditions, continued anxiety about forced repatriation, and uncertainties regarding resettlement can cause considerable stress for the refugees. Host country refugee policies are often dictated by domestic concerns, usually of a foreign policy nature and not necessarily determined by security and protection concerns or by the wishes of host communities in receiving countries (Tandon, 1984). There are many reports that refugee camps and internally displaced camps breed violence and people are often victims of violent acts perpetrated by the army, militias, humanitarian workers, and by their hosts (Malkki, 1995; Turner, 1999; UNHCR, 2002a). For many women and children, the very acts of going to communal latrines (Martin, 1991) or collecting firewood and water can be extremely dangerous.

| Summary What is organized violence? |
|---|
| Organized violence is violence with a systematic strategy. It is put into operation by members of groups with a centrally guided structure or political orientation (police units, rebel organizations, terror organizations, paramilitary and military formations). It is targeted for continuous use against individuals and groups who have different political attitudes, nationalities, or who come from specific racial, cultural, and ethnic backgrounds. It is characterized by the violation of human rights and disregard of women's and children's rights. The consequences reach far into the future of a society. |

## 2.1.4 The Concept of Post-Traumatic Stress Disorder (PTSD)

The pathological reactions to traumatic, stressful experiences are called "post-traumatic symptoms". The prefix "post-" means "after" or "later" – so "post-traumatic" means literally "after the injury" (of the soul). The study of the psychological consequences of traumatic events has a long tradition in psychiatry. In the 1970s, research studying the consequences of traumatic stress was stimulated by the finding that a large proportion of Vietnam veterans had major difficulties reintegrating into their pre-war roles. At the same time, researchers influenced by the women's movement responded to the observation of increased severe psychological problems in rape victims and began research in this area.

The current definition of PTSD in the DSM-IV (Diagnostics and Statistical Manual of Mental Disorders) outlines six criteria, which must be met at some level for a diagnosis of PTSD. They are as follows (refer also to the Summary Box):

(A) The first criterion refers to the *traumatic event*. PTSD can only be diagnosed when the symptoms are the result of some experienced or witnessed event that involved the actual or perceived threat of the life or physical integrity of the survivor or another person (A1). In addition, the immediate reaction of the victim must involve fear, terror, or helplessness (A2), i.e., include an alarm response.

(B) The second criterion is related to *intrusive symptoms*. In the context of PTSD, intrusive symptoms describe the chronic reliving of the event. This may come in the form of nightmares while one is sleeping or flashbacks that occur during waking hours. The phenomenon of reliving the event in the form of waking hour flashbacks, which are accompanied by multiple sensory experiences (hearing the bombs, feeling the weight of the bodies) as well as the sense of being back in the traumatic situation seems to be unique to PTSD (Brewin, 2001).

(C) This third criterion relates to the *avoidance behavior* associated with PTSD. Contrary to the current classification, a factor analysis (a statistical procedure which groups like variables) of PTSD symptoms suggested the subdivision of avoidance symptoms into two different groupings (Foa, Riggs, & Gershuny, 1995). The first factor (or grouping) includes *active avoidance* of reminders of the traumatic event. For instance, one might avoid people and places that are associated with the event or avoid talking or thinking about the event. The second factor relates to *passive avoidance* or *numbing*. These phenomena, which are also related to dissociation phenomena, include general emotional numbing as well as detachment from other people.

(D) The fourth criterion relates to a third group of symptoms. This group symptoms consists of the *arousal symptoms* (Criterion D). These symptoms result from an overall elevated level of arousal, which may come in the form of sleeping and concentration difficulties, an exaggerated startle response, or the enduring feeling of threat.

Note: The symptoms of Criterion B–D in PTSD do not automatically disappear in survivors as the PTSD resolves itself, but may persist for a long time.

(E) Criteria E sets a time frame for PTSD, as the symptoms must last for at least four weeks.

(F) Criterion F relates to the clinical significance of the disorder as it requires a remarkable reduction in day-to-day functioning for the diagnosis of PTSD. To decide whether the consequences of traumatic

---

| Summary | DSM-IV Criteria for PTSD |
|---|---|

**The 6 criteria for PTSD** (Diagnostic and Statistic Manual (DSM IV) of the American Psychiatric Association):
**Criterion A1** = experiencing or witnessing a life-threatening "traumatic event"
**Criterion A2** = subjective feelings of helplessness, fear or horror during that event
**Criterion B** = reliving or re-experiencing of the traumatic event - "Intrusions"
**Criterion C** = avoidance of reminders of the traumatic event - "Avoidance"
**Criterion D** = being overly aroused, alert, nervous – "Hyper-arousal"
**Criterion E** = a minimum of 4 weeks suffering from these consequences
**Criterion F** = severe problems in social, occupational, or other every day functioning

All criteria have to be fulfilled in order to diagnose Post-Traumatic Stress Disorder (PTSD).

| Summary | How does a traumatized person feel? |
|---|---|

Traumatization means suffering from a memory of a traumatic experience that has happened in the past. Re-experiencing the traumatic event means that the survivor involuntarily relives this situation, either while awake in the form of flashbacks or at night in the form of nightmares. Both are accompanied by intense feelings of fear and anger, often similar to the emotions that were experienced during the traumatic event itself. The body reacts in a stress response while remembering the event: the person's heart beats fast, they begin to sweat, painful bodily sensations might arise. The memories may come back repeatedly no matter how much the person does not want to remember. Flashbacks also can be experienced in different ways. The person may know quite well that the flashback is just a memory and feel safe in the here and now, or the person may not realize it is just a memory and may feel an intense feeling of fear and lack of safety. The person may actually believe the traumatic situation is happening again. In rare cases, this can last for up to tens of minutes. Some survivors describe that the memories pull them back into the past and that they are stuck in those moments of greatest fear. When nightmares occur, the survivor often awakes in a state of fear and can't go back to sleep again. Re-experiencing can be elicited by environmental cues, such as sounds or smells similar to those experienced during the traumatic event. Although the patient may not know exactly what triggered the memories, these same situations are often avoided in future. For instance, one may stop seeing certain people, stop going to certain places, or stop doing certain activities, all in an attempt to avoid reminders of the dreadful experiences. The patient may learn to be numb or to dissociate from reality, which may lead to a loss of loving feelings and of being able to feel close to people, even to one's own spouse or children. The patient may lose hope or may feel the future has nothing to hold. At the same time, the heightened level of arousal (excitement), resulting from permanent or repeatedly triggered fear, leads to states of increased alertness and readiness to counter danger at any time. Patients may become mistrustful and suspect danger everywhere or may have difficulties focusing their attention to activities of daily living or listening to others. When asked what they have just heard, read or seen, they may be unable to tell you.

events classify as a mental disorder rather than adaptive behavior, it is important to study the level of functional impairment that is associated with PTSD in the current environment of the survivor. Breslau (2001) compared the level of impairment associated with PTSD and other mental disorders (mainly other anxiety disorders and depression) on several indicators including current limitations in activities, missed work, self-assessed health, as well as desire to die. The PTSD patients presented with the worst outcome in respect to all criteria compared to both the individuals with other diagnoses and those without a diagnosis. A striking result from this study was that almost half (46%) of those who were diagnosed with PTSD reported that they had thought about suicide. Some 17% also reported completing a suicide attempt. PTSD also affects social functioning. Investigating the quality of intimate relationships of Vietnam veterans, Riggs and colleagues (1998) found that 70% of veterans who had been diagnosed with PTSD were in relationships characterized by clinically significant levels of relationship distress; this rate was much lower among veterans without PTSD (30%). In particular, veterans with PTSD presented more aggression towards their intimate partners and are at increased risk for perpetrating domestic violence (Byrne & Riggs, 1996).

### 2.1.5 Psychosocial Problems and Comorbid Disorders in Adults and Children

Another hypothesis regarding the functional impairment that results from and often accompanies PTSD is related to those symptoms that are not included in the DSM-IV diagnosis. These other symptoms may be related to comorbid mental disorders (disorders that occur simultaneously with PTSD, such as depression or anxiety; McFarlane, Atchison, Rafalowicz, & Papay, 1994). Epidemiological studies have found that one or more comorbid psychiatric disorders diagnosed in addition to PTSD occur in 80% of the cases (Kessler, 1995). Table 1 lists the disorders that often exist in parallel with PTSD.

Clinicians explain comorbid disorders in two ways. One is that the comorbid disorders occur independently as a result of the traumatic experience. For example, a victim may develop symptoms of depression following a traumatic loss. The other explanation is that the disorder is actually an extension of the core symptoms of PTSD. For instance, a victim who is experiencing vivid flashback-episodes might experience

**Table 1.** DSM-IV disorders frequently comorbid with PTSD (Kessler et al. 1995)

| Diagnosis | Lifetime Prevalence | Remarks |
|---|---|---|
| Major Depression | 48% | |
| Dysthymia | 22% | |
| Generalized Anxiety Disorder | 16% | |
| Simple Phobia | 30% | |
| Social Phobia | 28% | |
| Panic Disorder | 12.6% vs. 7.3% | women > men |
| Agoraphobia | 22.4% vs. 16.1% | women > men |
| Alcohol abuse/Dependence | 51.9% vs. 27.9% | men > women |
| Drug abuse/Dependence | 34.5% vs. 26.9% | men > women |
| Conduct Disorder | 43.3% vs. 15.4% | men > women |

a panic attack, indicative of panic disorder. Or, if someone feels detached and isolated from others, this person might abandon previous interests and hopes, start drinking or become clinically depressed. Another explanation for the comorbidity rates is that some underlying vulnerability present in an individual might increase the probability for that person to develop PTSD as well as other mental disorders.

In addition to experiencing psychosocial problems and mental health disorders, a child's normal healthy development also may be impaired. Factors such as altered memory function, frequent severe headaches, sleep disturbance, or loss of ability to concentrate may lead to a decline in school performance or difficulties in forming interpersonal relationships. In a survey of adolescents, Somasundaram (1993) found the following psychosocial problems and comorbid disorders as a consequence of these children being exposed to traumatic experiences during the war (Table 2).

**Table 2.** Psychosocial problems in Tamil adolescents (*N* = 625; Somasundaram, 1993)

| Psychosocial problem | No (%) |
|---|---|
| PTSD | 31 |
| Somatization | 32 |
| Anxiety | 34 |
| Depression | 29 |
| Hostility | 45 |
| Relationship problems | 34 |
| Alcohol and drug misuse | 7 |
| Functional disability | 35 |
| Loss of memory | 44 |
| Loss of concentration | 48 |
| Loss of motivation | 33 |

In one international, epidemiological survey among Tamil children (by vivo international, 2003), 57% of the children reported that traumatizing war experiences and the symptoms resulting from it interfered with their life. Social withdrawal, difficulties in leading a normal family life, and problems in school performance were most common. The greater the number of traumatic events reported, the greater the number of difficulties in social and emotional functioning reported by the child. Neuropsychological testing and school grades validated the outcome further and demonstrated the problem associated with this mental disorder. A psychological test of memory (the Rey-Osterrieth Complex Figure) revealed that nearly all children without PTSD scored perfectly, and were able to copy a figure by memory. However, interaction of PTSD diagnosis with recall shows that traumatized children are less able to perform well on this test and are unable to recall the different elements of the Rey Figure correctly. The recall score (% correctly recalled elements) dropped from 73% in the children without PTSD to 55% in those suffering from PTSD (Fig. 1).

Clinical interviews in this study (vivo international, 2003) further revealed that depressive symptoms were frequent in children with PTSD and 6 of the 16 children with PTSD had comorbid dysthymia (low-grade long-term depression). One child was diagnosed with a major depressive episode. In response to questions relating to affective disorders, only 12% of the children without PTSD reported symptoms of a mood disorder in comparison to 68% of those with PTSD. The risk of suicide was 26% in the children who presented with PTSD versus 7% in children without PTSD. Somatic symptoms (physical illness related symptoms) were also more frequently reported in children with PTSD than in those without PTSD. For

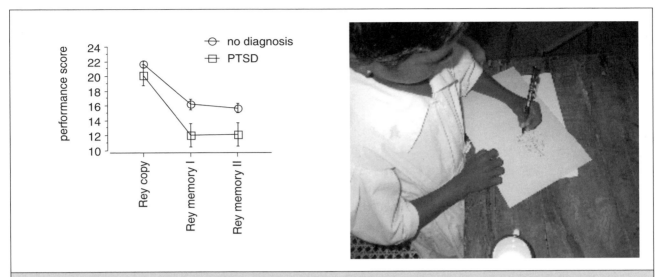

**Figure 1.** Children with and without PTSD can copy the Rey Figure equally well, but memory performance (right side: recall of the figure from memory) is better in children without PTSD (circles) than in those who present with PTSD (squares). From Elbert et al., in press.

instance, 81% of children with PTSD reported suffering from headaches during the last four weeks. In addition, children with PTSD had significantly lower school performance rates in key subjects compared to non-PTSD children (vivo Report, 2003).

Often, children are also indirectly affected by trauma. Their parents' and caretakers' symptoms of PTSD, such as emotional numbing and avoidance, prevent normal emotional feelings and loving behavior towards their children. As a result, family members of a traumatized person are forced to operate within a domestic context in which intimacy is severely impaired. In many cases, tension, domestic violence, and substance abuse increase. Children are more likely to be abused or neglected as a consequence. Furthermore, severe traumatic experiences have multigenerational effects. Some evidence suggests there are higher rates of anxiety and depression in children of survivors compared with non-traumatized comparison groups. However, more rigorous scientific studies are needed to uncover psychopathological consequences in the offspring of survivors.

### PTSD and Drug Abuse

Drug use and abuse is part of any discussion about mental health and PTSD. Substance use – e.g., alcohol, cigarettes, marihuana, cocaine, heroin, amphetamines, banji seeds – is by far the most predominant cause of premature and preventable illness, disability,

and death in most societies. Whereas abuse of and dependence on substances may in their own right bring suffering and physical sickness that require medical treatment, they often accompany other seemingly unrelated mental illnesses as well. PTSD patients tend to consume more drugs in an effort to reduce the suffering associated with their symptoms; however, in the long-term, substance abuse only adds to the suffering, bringing its own mental and physical anguish. If drug abuse is found in children and adolescents, it is always a "cry for help" and should not be punished as such. It is of key importance to emphatically explore the reasons for such behavior together with the troubled youngster. Traumatic events, but also suffering related to neglect or abuse during childhood years, are likely causes. A number of treatment programs exist that can reach the substance abuser and his or her family.

### PTSD and Physical Illness

The relationship between stress and physical illnesses, in particular infectious diseases, has been well established (see Section 1.1.2) and there are several assumptions about the immunological mechanisms that may be responsible for this effect (Kiecolt-Glaser, 2002). Given that PTSD is a chronic stressor for a person, it will exert its adverse effects on the health of the individual. Therefore, traumatization also causes increased risk for the functioning of the cardiovascular, gastrointestinal, endocrinological, and musclular-skeletal systems (Schnurr, 2002). Exposure to trauma can also lead to problems with pain perception, pain tolerance, and chronic pain.

### Vulnerability for PTSD

Epidemiological studies showed that not everyone who experiences a traumatic event develops chronic PTSD; on the contrary, PTSD is the exception rather than the rule to a single traumatic exposure. The most adverse single event seems to be rape as it leads to PTSD in about half the victims, followed by participation in war (two out of five individuals), and childhood abuse (more than one third) (Kessler, 1995). The fact that only a fraction of survivors of a traumatic event later develop PTSD has stimulated research into predictors for its development. Pre-trauma vulnerability factors like education, previous trauma, childhood adversity, psychiatric history, and family psychiatric history predicted PTSD consistently over several studies, but only to a surprisingly small extent. Factors operating during the event, such as trauma severity, or immediately after the event, such as lack of social support, seem to have stronger effect sizes, but still their explanatory power is small. The original conceptualization of PTSD was based on the implicit assumption that the traumatic event is the main agent for the development of PTSD (Yehuda, 1995). The idea was that traumatic events could cause PTSD in anyone regardless of pre-trauma vulnerability.

Even studies that researched PTSD in those who experienced the most adverse events, like torture or incarceration in a concentration camp, find PTSD prevalence rates in less than half of the sample (Basoglu, 1994). While it can be doubted that there are single events that cause chronic PTSD in all victims, some studies show that *a history of previous traumatic events increases the probability of developing PTSD after a subsequent event* (Brewin, 2000). We carried out a study that showed that the cumulative number of traumatic events experienced was the main predictor of PTSD among the war-affected Sudanese and Ugandan West-Nile populations. In the studied population, we found that every person who reported more than some 25 traumatic events in the lifetime met the criteria for PTSD. Nobody seems to be resilient at such a level of repeated threat (Schauer et al., 2003; Neuner et al., 2004). This means that PTSD has a "building block" effect and that exposure to trauma and violence is cumulative or additive, contributing to the development of PTSD over time, given a high enough "dose" of trauma (Schauer et al.,

2003). This building block effect has recently been replicated by Onyut et al. (2004b) for samples of Rwandan and Somali refugees.

### Culture and PTSD

There is no evidence for the hypothesis that the prevalence and validity of PTSD depends on cultural factors. Contrary to the statements by some psychiatrists, such as Summerfield and colleagues who postulate that there is no universal trauma response, current research into the epidemiology of PTSD and the neurobiological mechanisms behind PTSD offer strong arguments for the hypothesis that PTSD is a pathological consequence of traumatic events that occurs in all cultures. Obviously, this possibility to break the mind is an integral part of being human. There are studies of PTSD from all continents, and local experts from all continents have contributed to the research in this field.

Some people have argued that the transfer of western concepts and techniques to war-affected societies in developing countries risks "perpetuating the colonial status of the non-western mind" as every "culture has its own frameworks for mental health, and norms for help-seeking at times of crisis" (Summerfield, 1997, p. 1568). This argument is based on a clear distinction between western "eurocentric" cultures and other cultures in non-industrialized countries. This distinction may seem to be straightforward, but is not valid. Viewing culture as a particular civilization at a particular stage, there is always a wide diversity of attitudes, values, and habits, and neither frontiers between countries nor between the industrialized and non-industrialized world can offer valid borderlines of cultural categories. The same is true for health and mental concepts. Many societies in developing countries have already chosen to adapt mental health concepts developed by western psychology and psychiatry and prefer the corresponding treatment methods rather than or in combination with traditional healing. At the same time, in many rural areas in European countries traditional healing techniques for physical and mental complaints have remained popular.

Those clinicians who emphasize the differences between cultures and advocate non-interference in cultures that are considered to be "traditional" use ethical arguments. Terms such as "culturally sensitive" are now included in mental health proposals and articles as matter of political correctness. Even on moral grounds it is not straightforward to favor the position of not interfering in cultural traditions, norms, and beliefs in psychosocial work. All cultures are constantly changing and the idea that there are any cultures that fully rely on traditional norms and have not been affected by the modern world is nothing more than the romantic view of western minds. The consequences of not interfering in cultural norms would also include withholding knowledge about general scientific methods of objective assessment and evaluation from these cultures.

*There are considerable similarities and consistencies in the clinical manifestations of psychopathology across different refugee groups; these similarities and consistencies outweigh cultural and ethnic differences. Knowledge of this should lead us away from treating the mental health difficulties of refugees as something new and unusual while allowing us to focus attention on developing culturally sensitive assessment and treatment approaches to meet the special needs.*

Garcia-Peltoniemi (1991)

It is these methods that have led to the development of treatment approaches that have proven to be effective and that have led to the identification of less successful or even harmful methods in many fields of healing and medicine. Withholding this knowledge from resource-poor countries might help to leave cultural norms untouched, but at the same time the global discrepancies in development and power remain unchanged. Protecting societies that are considered to be traditional from modern influences risks building cultural reservations of societies that remain dependent on the goodwill of the powerful countries.

There is now considerable knowledge about the epidemiology and validity of the PTSD concept in a wide variety of cultures. Until now, however, there have been few treatment studies, besides those performed by vivo, that have evaluated the efficacy of different approaches in war-affected populations in developing countries. At this level of knowledge, it is an ethical obligation of psychosocial organizations to concentrate research on how the problem of mental health in these societies can be approached most effectively. The practice of many organizations that implement large-scale psychosocial projects with non-evaluated treatment approaches is unacceptable. The alternative, however, is to demand more research instead of supporting a blanket rejection of current approaches in the field of mental health.

### 2.1.6 Complex PTSD

Classifying the diversity of traumatic events according to their impact, Herman (1992) has suggested differentiating between two different types of traumas. Type I traumatic events are those events that lead to pathological consequences after a single exposure, like a car accident or an isolated rape. The more severe Type II events include those that happen repeat-

---

**Summary     Complex PTSD**

**I. Alteration in regulation of affect and impulses**
A. Chronic affect dysregulation
B. Difficulty modulating anger
C. Self-destructive and suicidal behavior
D. Difficulty modulating sexual involvement
E. Impulsive and risk-taking behaviors

**II. Alterations in attention or consciousness**
A. Amnesia
B. Transient dissociative episodes and depersonalization

**III. Somatization**
A. Digestive system
B. Chronic pain
C. Cardiopulmonary symptoms
D. Conversion symptoms
E. Sexual symptoms

**IV. Alteration in self-perception**
A. Chronic guilt, shame and self-blame
B. Feelings of being permanently damaged
C. Feeling ineffective
D Feeling nobody can understand
E. Minimizing the importance of the traumatic event

**V. Alterations in perception of the perpetrator** (not needed for diagnosis)
A. Adopting distorted beliefs
B. Idealization of the perpetrator
C. Preoccupation with hurting the perpetrator

**VI. Alterations in relation with others**
A. Inability to trust
B. Revictimization
C. Victimizing others

**VII. Alterations in systems of meaning**
A. Despair, hopelessness
B. Loss of previously sustaining beliefs

edly over an extended time period, accounting for symptoms experienced by survivors of torture, childhood sexual abuse, or prisoner-of-war camps. In these cases, victims could foresee the next traumatic experience but could not influence the timing and had no way of escaping other than through dissociation of consciousness. This leads to comorbid problems and clinical symptoms in addition and beyond the symptom triad of intrusion, avoidance, and arousal. As described before, enduring personality changes may occur (see International Classification of Disorders/ICD-10 F62.0). Such "complex PTSD" was subsequently also called "disorder of extreme stress" (DES) (Herman, 1992; van der Kolk, 1993; Pelcovitz et al., 1997).

## 2.2  PTSD and Memory

*Give sorrow words:*
*The grief that does not speak*
*Whispers the o'er-fraught heart,*
*And bids it break*
William Shakespeare, Macbeth

### 2.2.1  The Nature of Traumatic Memory

For the development of effective treatment methods, it is essential to understand the psychological and biological processes that underlie PTSD. Some key features of memories of traumatic events emphasize the relevance of memory processes for the explanation of PTSD.

The most distinct symptom of PTSD is the re-experiencing of the traumatic event in the form of flashbacks. These involuntary intrusions can be triggered by cues that remind a person of the traumatic situation. The reliving can include all kinds of sensory information, like pictures, sounds, smells and bodily sensations (Terr, 1993; van der Kolk, 1995). A feature of flashbacks is the feeling that this event is happening again right at that moment. This means that during a flashback victims are not fully aware that what they are experiencing is a memory from the past; on the contrary, they think they are back in the situation. The memory of the traumatic event does not seem to be fixed in the context of time and space in which it actually occurred (Ehlers & Clark, 2000).

The person may see, feel, or hear the sensory elements of the traumatic experience, yet he or she may be prevented from being able to translate this experi-

ence into communicable language. Despite the fact that patients report frequent episodes of reliving the experience through flashbacks or nightmares, it is extremely difficult for them to narrate the event in a detailed and consistent manner. Patients report that they can remember the event all too well, as they suffer from painful involuntary recollections. However, if asked to report the event, the narrations are typically disorganized, fragmented, and incoherent (van der Kolk, 1995). As Herman (1992) puts it, humans who have survived atrocities often tell their stories in a highly emotional, contradictory, and fragmented manner which undermines their credibility and thereby serves the twin imperatives of truth-telling and secrecy. Survivors can begin their recovery only when the truth is finally acknowledged. But, "... secrecy prevails, and the story of the traumatic event surfaces not as a verbal narrative but as a symptom" (Herman, 1992).

Harvey and Bryant (1999) showed that the disorganization of the narration is correlated with symptoms of acute stress disorder. Systematic observations found evidence that there is a breakdown in the ability to put the most emotional part of the traumatic event, a period of time which could have lasted anywhere from several seconds to several hours, into words. Bessel van der Kolk (1997) has argued that trauma is experienced as "timeless and ego-alien." Victims literally may be out of touch with their feelings. Physiologically, they may respond as if they are being traumatized again, but this may be dissociated from semantic knowledge, not part of the explicit memory. If the victim experiences de-realization he cannot "own" what is happening, and thus cannot take steps to do anything about it.

For survivors of longer-lasting events and for those who were exposed to a series of traumatic events, as is often the case for victims of organized violence, this problem in narrating one's history can persist for a long period of time. This effect was described by Rosenthal (1997), who documented the life-stories of Holocaust survivors:

*It is difficult to establish a relationship between the different stages of life – this means the time before the persecution, the time of persecution and the time after having survived. Within these stages, the relationship of the different events can be substantially broken into pieces. Whole stages can sink into the sphere of speechlessness and are accessible for the biographer only in single fragments, pictures and moods.* (p. 40)

Thus, the characteristic of the memory of a traumatic event is twofold: On the one hand, a person has very vivid recollections of the event including many sensory details; on the other hand, it is very difficult for the victim to face the memories and to learn to put the details into coherent speech and chronological order. This is because traumatic events are stored differently than memories of everyday events. This pathological representation of traumatic memories is what is responsible for the core symptoms of PTSD (Brewin, 2001; Brewin, Dalgleish, & Joseph, 1996; Ehlers & Clark, 2000; Metcalfe & Jacobs, 1996; van der Kolk, 1996). This difference in storage of memories will be addressed next.

In order to understand the pathological characteristics of traumatic memories, it is first necessary to understand how normal past events are stored in memory. Based on neuropsychological research, Squire (1994) differentiated two types of memory, *declarative* (explicit) and *non-declarative* (implicit). Declarative memory consists of memory of personal events, as well as memory of facts and knowledge of the world. For instance, declarative memory represents significant events like a marriage or a graduation as well as knowledge about the history or geography of the world. In contrast, non-declarative memory covers skills, habits, emotional associations and conditioned responses. Based on this taxonomy of memory, Squire (1994) determined that declarative or explicit memories can be deliberately retrieved, whereas non-declarative or implicit memories are not deliberately retrieved and do not require conscious recollection. Non-declarative memories do have an impact on a person's behavior and experiences, but are activated through other processes, such as environmental or internal cues, similar to those memories of trauma survivors.

Using the example of declarative memory, we know that the memory of a wedding or the story of the French Revolution can be deliberately retrieved or activated when desired (assuming one was paying attention in history class!). However non-declarative memories do not involve a deliberate recall. For example, for most people, opening a door is a highly practiced skill that is automatically activated without ever remembering how and when that skill was learned. The memory of a traumatic event can be triggered by an external cue such as a smell or a sound. Putting these two types of memory together, we can see that a single event can be stored as two different types of memory. For instance, a person learns to ride a bike. The day that the rider learned to ride the bike is stored in that person's memory as a historical event

in that person's life. This is an example of declarative memory. However, as the person becomes more adept at bike riding, it is no longer necessary to remember each step of riding the bike. Riding a bike thus becomes a skill that is easily activated without deliberate recall. It is coded as a non-declarative memory.

Tulving (2001) further distinguished *episodic* and *semantic* memory. As the name implies, episodic memories are stored as episodes, i.e., happenings in particular places at particular times and covers information about "what," "where," and "when". Tied to episodic memory is the re-collective experience. Episodic memory allows people to consciously re-experience one's previous events and to activate the sensory-perceptual experience. In contrast, semantic memory is our knowledge base, for instance, it might include knowing that five times 12 equals 60 or that Greenland is covered with ice. This type of memory is not necessarily related to experience in the sense that a visit to Greenland has to be made to build up the respective semantic representation.

### 2.2.2 Sensory-Perceptual Representation

If you think about past life events, you may not only retrieve abstract knowledge about what has happened ("On September 21st, I went to Jaffna by boat"), but also sometimes imagine (Lang, 1979) the event in the form of a "recollective experience" (Tulving, 2001) ("I feel the breeze over the water, the swinging of the boat"). In the case of recalling the event as a recollective experience, you directly accessed visual and other sensory information about past events previously stored in your mind, in addition to being aware of the sequence of events that happened.

Obviously, this form of vivid and detailed recollection is not possible for all events experienced in life. For everyday events, which have less significance to a person, these representations usually only last minutes or hours (Conway, 2001). They can only become more stable if they are integrated with other memory structures. In this case, detailed images of this event can be retrieved years later. This enduring storage of sensory-perceptual representations only happens for events stored in a highly emotional state, as this meant that they are significant for the achievement or failure of individual goals (Conway & Pleydell-Pearce, 2000).

Lang's bio-informational theory of emotion (Lang, 1979) offers a good framework, within which to un-

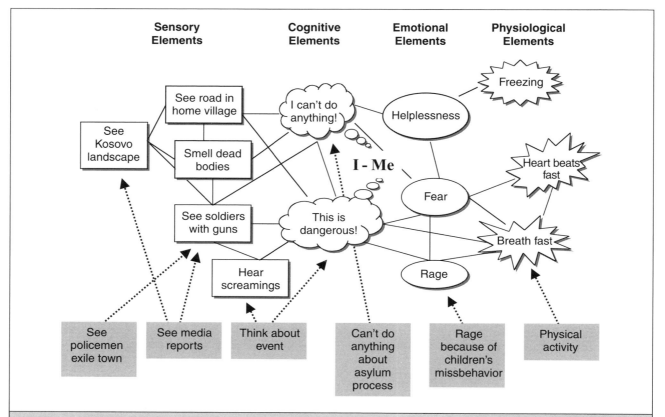

**Figure 2.** Schematic presentation of a hypothetical sensory-perceptual representation – a so-called "fear network," including sensory, cognitive, emotional, and physiological elements. The network represents a Kosovar refugee's memory of the attack on his home village. The boxes below indicate environmental stimuli with the potential to activate the representation.

derstand the nature of sensory-perceptual representations and their embedding emotions. In this view, emotions are considered "response propositions" or more general action dispositions, i.e., modes in neural networks (neuronal connections within the brain) that favor distinct sets of actions.

These representations consist of sensory-perceptual information about the stimuli present in the past situation in different modalities (visual, auditory, olfactory, etc.). In other words, a single traumatic memory can be experienced by a victim in many different ways, all simultaneously. At the same time as a person is experiencing the sensory aspects of the memory, for instance, other parts of this network or system within the brain are processing cognitive or emotional information in response to the stimuli. Additionally, the body is also responding with a set of corresponding physiological reactions. Another set of "response propositions" include the motor and physiological responses to the stimulus or memory. All elements of this network of brain activity are connected such that

the activation of a single item (such as a sensory experience) leads to an activation of other elements (see Figure 2 as an example).

The sensory-perceptual representations of traumatic events have also been called *fear structures*. Lang (1979, 1984, 1993) concluded that *fear structures* or *fear networks* operate in anxiety disorders. This theory explains the ability to remember and relive past events in the form of "recollective experiences" (in which the subjective, sensory components of memory are experienced, as conceptualized by Tulving, 2001). In addition, this model predicts that these recollections of the event would occur simultaneously with physiological and emotional responses similar to those that occurred when the event happened. For instance, if someone experienced great levels of fear and terror accompanied by heart palpitations while watching a horrible event, this fear and terror and the heart palpitations would be relived upon remembering the event. These predictions have been confirmed by Lang (1979, 1984, 1993) and co-workers using subjective, behavioral, and physiological measurements during mental imagery.

Conway (2001) stated that the retrieval of a sensory-perceptual representation, a memory with sensory information, is the final step in recalling a memory of a past event. He asserts that this process of recovering sensory information takes some effort on the part of the individual and that the process lasts for several seconds of time, rather than occurring instantaneously. However, the impact of emotional structures on behavior is not limited to the deliberate retrieval of memories of past events, as for instance during voluntary mental imagery. Elements of the structure can also be automatically retrieved by a cue and lead to emotional behavior. For instance, the smell of dead bodies may activate pictures of a road in the home village in the network of Figure 2, without the person choosing to bring these pictures back to mind. Edna Foa and Mike Kozak, a Lang scholar, have related the network theory to PTSD (Foa & Kozak, 1986), whereby a PTSD network would differ from representations (the coding of memories) of normal events in several ways:

- Fear structures encoded during a traumatic event are unusually large (including many nodes or neural elements within the brain) and cover a wide variety of single elements being coded, such as sight, sound, emotions, physical sensations. This means that nodes in the fear structures can be easily activated, as many stimuli in the environment have similarities to one or the other element and thus can act as cues.
- Interconnections between single elements, such as sight and sound, are unusually powerful. Consequently, the ignition of only a single element, such as a firecracker exploding, may be sufficient to activate the whole structure, causing all of the related memories to return. This explains why traumatized people can have sudden flashbacks when reminded of the traumatic event. According to this theory, an environmental stimulus or internal cue, like thinking about the event or an intense heart beat that resembles one part of the stimulus configuration of the traumatic situation can cause the full firing of the sensory information. In turn, the associated emotional, physiological, and motor responses stored in the fear structure will also be triggered. According to this theory, a flashback is the activation of the entire fear network.

In addition to phenomena of intrusive recollections, this theory can also explain the typical PTSD symptom of avoidance. The activation of a fear structure is experienced as a fearful and painful recollection, and consequently many PTSD patients learn to prevent this by avoiding cues that remind them of the traumatic event. They learn to avoid both internal and external cues, so they try not to think about it, not to talk about it, and to keep away from persons and places that remind them of the event. In addition, running away or other types of motoric flight behavior (feeling the need to flee a specific situation) can be part of the fear structure. The potential of physiological arousal to trigger the fear network can be so strong that any affective arousal, even positive emotions, are avoided. The victim seems to have become emotionally numb.

### 2.2.3 Autobiographical Contextual Memory

The sensory-perceptual representation is only one type of memory about past experiences. When a person retrieves a memory about a past event, the type of memory that is generally retrieved first is called *autobiographical memory* (Conway & Pleydell-Pearce, 2000). At the top of the hierarchy of autobiographical memory organization is the memory of *lifetime periods*. Lifetime periods represent general knowledge of persons, places, actions, activities, plans, or goals that characterize a special period. They cover distinct time periods with identifiable beginnings and endings. An example of a lifetime period is "The time when I lived with Mary." Lifetime periods are typically organized along major themes of persons who are related to goals in life. Typical themes include relationships, occupations, and places one lived. Lifetime periods related to different themes can overlap with respect to the time period to which they refer. For example, the time covered by "When I was working at the farm" may overlap with the time span of "When I lived with Mary."

A type of knowledge base, or classification of memories, one step down from lifetime periods is the memory of *general events*. General events can be divided into repeated events like "Having lunch at the cafeteria" or single events like "My first day at school." These knowledge bases organize the sequence of events. Not all events a person experiences are represented with the same accuracy. Shum (1998) suggested that those events demarcating beginnings and ends of lifetime periods play a significant role in defining autobiographical memories. These landmark events (like the first date with a subsequent intimate partner or the struggle that indicated the end of a relationship) are thought to be represented in more detail and accessed more easily. Memories of activities that cover a series of events related to a common theme can be connected to form so-called "mini-histories" (Robinson, 1992). For example, the mini-history of "my first love" consists of a set of memories of related events like "my first date" and "my first kiss."

Continuing down the hierarchy of memory, Conway and Pleydell-Pearce (2000) define *event-specific knowledge*. This knowledge corresponds to the sensory-perceptual representations described above, such as when my mother was taking me to school (on my first day at school). Event specific knowledge (mother was taking me to school) is usually linked to general event structures (my first day at school), and the activation of the sensory-perceptual details of an event (e.g., the picture of the classroom) is accompanied by the activation of knowledge about the sequence of the event (first we went to school and then I saw the classroom) and the location of the event in lifetime periods (we still lived in our homeland then).

Taking this new understanding of memory, we can now look at PTSD and how memory is affected. First, we will take a close look at how autobiographical memory, general memory, and lifetime periods are all affected in persons with PTSD. The first assumption is that patients who suffer from PTSD have a *significant distortion in their autobiographical memory*. In contrast to those who remember major events as general events, there is evidence to suggest that in persons with PTSD, the traumatic event is *not* clearly represented as a general event. Furthermore, the event does not seem to be clearly positioned in a lifetime period. Even though one's memories and the sensory-perceptual representations of traumatic events are very strong and long lasting, there does not seem to be a reliable autobiographical structure within which the memory falls. Because the ability to recall one's life history in the form of a well-organized autobiographical memory is necessary in order to narrate an event, PTSD patients are often unable to narrate their traumatic experiences. The result is a disorganization and distortion of the sequence of autobiographical memories.

In this passage, Metcalfe and Jacobs (1996) describe the typical characteristics of an isolated activation of a sensory-perceptual representation for patients with PTSD:

*Memories and reactions that are attributable to the isolated hot-system encoding may seem irrational both to the individual him- or herself, and to the therapist, since such fragments are ungrounded by the kind of narrative and spatio-temporal contextual*

*anchors that tie our ordinary experience to reality. Such memories are disturbing, not only because of the direct fear they evoke, but also because of their strangeness.* (p. 2)

The sensory-perceptual-emotional representations of the traumatic event have also been called *hot memory* (Metcalfe & Jacobs, 1996) or *situationally accessible memory*, whereas the autobiographical context memory has been called *cold memory* or *verbally accessible memory*.

---

**Summary        PTSD and Memory**

During a traumatic event mainly sensory and perceptual information (for example, the sound of bullet shots, the smell of blood) is stored in memory during a highly emotional state. The mind and body become extremely aroused (rapid heartbeat, sweating, trembling) and are set for action, like hiding, fighting, or running away. This emotional and sensory information is stored separately from the information related to the content. It is stored in a interconnected neural network from which a so-called "fear network" is established. The fear network includes sensory, cognitive, physiological, and emotional experiences, including the action disposition related to the experience (= hot memory, situationally accessible memory, sensory perceptual representation). Environmental stimuli (e.g., a smell or noise) and internal cues (e.g., a thought) can activate this fear structure later at any given time. The ignition of only a few elements in the network is sufficient to activate the whole structure. This is thought to be a "flashback," i.e., the feeling as if one is back in the traumatic situation with its sounds, smells, feelings of fear, response propositions, and thoughts. Since the activation of the fear network is a frightening and painful recollection, many PTSD patients learn to avoid cues that act as reminders of the traumatic event. They try not to think about any part represented in the fear network, not to talk about it, and to keep away from persons and places that remind them of the frightening event. In contrast to the extensive fear memory, patients who suffer from PTSD have difficulties with autobiographical memory; that is, they are unable to place the fear of the events appropriately in time and space and to clearly position them in a lifetime period. This, and the avoidance of activating the fear structure, makes it difficult for PTSD patients to narrate their traumatic experience.

### 2.2.4 Neurobiological Basis of Memory and PTSD

Neuroimaging studies have demonstrated significant neurobiological changes in PTSD. There appear to be four areas of the brain in particular that are different in patients with PTSD compared with those in control subjects: the *hippocampus*, the *amygdala*, and the *medial frontal* and *the anterior cingulate cortex*. The medial temporal lobe and the connected hippocampus are brain structures that play a major role in the transformation and construction of (cold) memories that contain autobiographical information, including the temporal and spatial context of an event, while the amygdala and cingulated cortex are relevant for hot memories. Together with the controlling frontal lobe structures, these structures are important for the development and processing of emotions.

How memories are formed and coded within the brain is the next step in understanding the potential impairment that might occur with a person suffering from PTSD. First of all, Shastri (2002) shows that it is essential to be able to transform the single events a person experiences into a "conjunctive code" within the brain. This conjunctive code is a meaningful cognitive representation of the information an individual experiences within a certain space and time – without this coding, memories and experiences would be meaningless. McClelland and colleagues (1995) suggested that the hippocampus is especially important for the coding of information that contradicts previously learned knowledge. This is especially important for survivors of traumatic experiences, as much of what they experience during times of trauma contradicts basic assumptions that have been learned in life about security, trust, and human nature.

In terms of PTSD, the amygdala is important because it appears to be hyper-reactive to trauma-related stimuli. In turn, higher brain regions, such as the hippocampus and the medial frontal cortex, are affected as they are unable to handle the overload of stimuli that results from symptoms such as an exaggerated startle response and flashbacks. Stress hormones that result from these experiences impair the ability of the brain function properly and to create memories correctly. Based on research with rodents (for a review, see, e.g., McEwen, 2002), there is evidence that the stress hormones released during traumatic events affects both the function and the structure of the hippocampus. Exposure to *glucocorticoids* (stress hormones that occur during traumatic events) normally increases the activity of the hippocampus; however, if

a certain threshold is exceeded the functioning begins to decline drastically. Under very high levels of stress, the functioning of the hippocampus becomes severely impaired and the hippocampus, along with the medial frontal cortex, are unable to mediate the exaggerated symptoms of arousal and distress that occur in the amygdala in response to reminders of the traumatic event (Nutt & Malizia, 2004). It is assumed that very high doses of adrenal steroids may even cause permanent and irreversible atrophy (decrease in size) of the hippocampus (McEwen, 1999; Kim & Yoon, 1998).

Consistent with these findings, some, but not all, neuroimaging studies have found that the hippocampus is smaller in individuals with PTSD than in comparison subjects (Bremner et al., 1997, 2003). However, some of these studies, which were performed in veterans, failed to control for alcohol use, a behavior known to be higher in patients with PTSD than in controls. Other studies found changes in the limbic cortex, and particularly in the anterior cingulated cortex. Some authors have argued that the cause-effect relationship is preexisting; i.e., that an individual with a smaller hippocampus may be more prone to develop PTSD when exposed to a traumatic event – these researchers explored whether or not a reduction in the volume of the hippocampus occurs in survivors of a recent trauma who develop PTSD. Shalev and his group found that smaller hippocampal volume is not a preexisting risk factor for the development of PTSD, but that it later occurs in individuals with chronic or complicated PTSD (Bonne, 2001).

In our own research, we have identified dysfunctional brain areas in survivors of organized violence (Elbert et al., 2003; Rockstroh et al., in press). Abnormal electromagnetic slow waves in the brain (1–5 Hz) often surround circumscribed pathological or dysfunctional brain regions. Using ASWAM (Abnormal Slow Wave Mapping – Figure 3), we examined the extent of local clustering of magnetic slow wave generators in a variety of neurological and psychiatric diseases and mapped deafferented and dysfunctional brain regions. In a sample of 48 victims of severe and repeated torture, we observed a 94% prevalence of PTSD. In these survivors of severe violence, significant functional alteration and dysfunctional networks were observed in (left) fronto-temporal regions. In contrast, depressive patients, investigated with the same technique and protocol, exhibited less frontal activity than either controls or other PTSD patients.

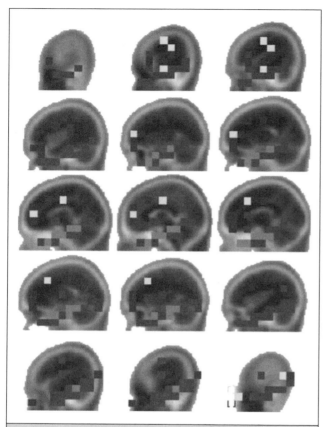

**Figure 3.** Abnormal brain waves have been recorded and localized in a brain of a torture victim using magnetic source imaging. Volume elements (voxels) where abnormal brain waves are generated have been marked with different shades of grey. (Data from our clinic)

---

**Summary     PTSD and the Brain**

The functioning of brain structures important for memory coding, like the hippocampus, is strongly affected by traumatic stress and stress hormones. Under very high levels of traumatic stress the function of the hippocampus and related neural networks is impaired. Hence, during times of severe stress the autobiographical memory storage is distorted. The more difficult a stressor is emotionally, the more active those areas of the brain encode emotional content become. During a traumatic event, the amygdala – the structure in the brain that prepares the body for danger – and the interconnected frontal lobe regions respond to the stimuli of the event. The individual then is "overconditioned" to respond to fear. This may explain the exaggerated emotional responses to fear situations in PTSD patients.

## 2.3   Processing of Affective Experiences

### 2.3.1   Normal Emotional Processing

Whereas most people react with an intensive emotional upheaval immediately following a traumatic event, including symptoms of acute stress and PTSD symptoms, only a minority of this population fully develops chronic PTSD. The recovery from acute stress symptoms seems to be the usual process in most human beings. Several authors have tried to identify the mechanisms behind this emotional processing, as this information may lead to the development of effective treatment options for chronic PTSD. In an influential work on the topic, Foa & Kozak, (1986) suggested that *emotional processing* involves a modification of the original fear structure; in other words, the fear structure, or the complete process of cognitive, psychological, and physiological events that occur when a person is remembering a fearful event, is modified such that the complete fear structure is no longer triggered by current events and stimuli (see Section 2.2.2 for a discussion of fear structures).

In order for the victim to recover from the debilitating effects of PTSD, the brain must begin to *inhibit the fear response,* leading to an *extinction of the fear response.* One theory is that by activating the fear structure in a safe context, for example, by allowing the memories to be triggered with another person present, this process can begin to take place. Triggering the memories in a momentarily safe environment allows for the possibility of introducing new elements, ones that are incompatible with the original fear-based connections, into the existing fear structure. For example, the newly-introduced thought, or cognition, "I am safe" contradicts the main cognitive elements of the fear structure that have been resulting in a permanent state of impending threat. By allowing the individual to experience the current fear structure in conjunction with the current incompatible information, the fear structure can be modified such that maladaptive associations between the stimulus (fearful memories) and response (symptoms of PTSD) decrease over time. In other words, by exposing the individual to both the triggers to the fearful memories of the trauma, along with new contradictory information, the fear will begin to lessen over time as the new information is integrated. Normally, this process of integration occurs naturally after an emotional event without any specific intervention, but in the case of extreme trauma, this process may be inhibited due to an avoidance of the fear structure or because the individual prematurely terminates the process out of fear of the stimuli. On the other hand, the *inhibition of emotional processing* leads to a maintenance of the fear structure and the development of chronic PTSD.

Research on *fear conditioning* has challenged this view. Several investigators have shown that an *extinction or elimination of fear responses* will not necessarily change the original stimulus-fear associations, as the original fear response can easily be reinstated in a context different to the context of extinction learning. For example, just because an individual has become accustomed or desensitized to hearing fireworks does not mean that a repeated traumatic event will not reinstate the original fear structure. Instead, extinction probably occurs through the inhibition of the fear response by a *regulative process* (LeDoux, 2000). This regulative process is based on a more thorough evaluation of the current situation than the automatic evaluation by the fear structure, that is, the brain is able to process the information about the event more slowly and thoroughly rather than just reacting emotionally to the information. Brewin (2001) suggested that this cortical evaluation depends on the availability of declarative memory of the stimulus. By using the information from declarative memory about the past event, the individual is better able to evaluate whether the current stimulus indicates a threat.

As noted above, after a traumatic event, declarative knowledge, and especially autobiographical knowledge, which offers information about the context of the feared stimulus, is fragmented or even absent. This can lead to a lack of capability for the *cortical inhibition of the fear response*. The process of cortical inhibition of the conditioned fear response occurs as the person learns to distinguish between past and present threats. In other words, the person who experienced a traumatic event in the past learns that stimuli in the presents are not currently a threat. In normal emotional processing, the intrusive memories provide an opportunity for the individual to build up declarative memory about the event. As the person thinks and talks about this event, utilizing and integrating the memories and the stimuli presented by intrusive memories, cortical inhibition begins to take place, and more functional and accurate autobiographical knowledge can be constructed about the traumatic episode.

The construction of autobiographical knowledge about the traumatic event is no easy task as the organization of autobiographic knowledge is connected to personal goals and to basic beliefs about the self. This means that active emotional processing takes time and effort. Secondary emotions like anger and guilt may indicate problems in the cognitive processing of the event and the adaptive placement of the traumatic experience in the context of preexisting beliefs about the self, which also interferes with the construction of a coherent autobiographical representation. Because thinking about the traumatic event automatically causes painful emotions, many people avoid this process and try to eliminate intrusive memories as soon as possible. The fact that victims with poor social support following a traumatic event are at an increased risk for developing PTSD (Ozer, Best, Lipsey, & Weiss, 2003) might be explained by the lack of opportunity or encouragement to talk about the event. Persons who do not have strong support networks may be less likely to talk about the event, which, within a strict definition of the term, allows for emotional processing and the chronological reconstruction of autobiographical memory.

| Summary | Emotional Processing of the Fear Structure |
|---|---|

Emotional processing probably does not involve the modification of the original fear structure. Instead, emotional processing enables the reconstruction of the autobiographical representation of the event. The explicit (declarative) autobiographical representation is needed to regulate the activation of the original fear structure. People naturally seem to try to heal themselves by narrating their experience. In many cases this is helpful, because this process naturally helps building up "cool memory" context information. Because thinking about the traumatic event automatically causes painful emotions, people avoid this process (despite the fact that it may prove helpful) and try to terminate recollection as soon as possible. By avoiding the memories, they are inhibiting the habitual processing of the experience and as a result the fear structure seems to consolidate itself and chronic PTSD can develop. When, however, a patient thinks and talks about the event in chronological order and includes the stimuli presented by intrusive memories, autobiographical knowledge about the traumatic episode can be reconstructed and the victim can learn to distinguish between past and current threats. The construction of a narration enforces the activation and consequently habituation of the fear. This exposure is the most powerful means to "tearing down" the fear network. In this process, the patient is learning that sensory and emotional memory can be activated without fear.

### 2.3.2 Implications for Treatment

Quite a number of treatment approaches intend to relieve trauma symptoms by purposefully visualizing the traumatic events. Some successfully reduce symptomatology having the survivor tell the worst event repeatedly in detail (Bisbey & Bisbey, 1998). Foa and colleagues (1998) systematically developed *exposure therapy* for PTSD. This technique has proven to be one of the most successful treatment approaches for this disorder. When implementing exposure therapy for PTSD, the patient is instructed to repeatedly talk about the traumatic experience, thus exposing the individual to the event and memories. In particular, Foa (1995) demonstrated that those patients who manage to construct a coherent narrative of the event during exposure therapy profit most from treatment.

The main focus of this therapy should be on the part of the memory that is most fragmented in autobiography and most intensively represented in sensory-perceptual representations. These moments of intense recollection of memories, complete with physical sensations, have often been referred to as "hot spots". In order for the victim to form a consistent autobiographical narration of this moment, the *sensory-perceptual representations* (*memories of physical sensations*) are inevitably activated, as they provide detailed knowledge about the event that is not yet available in *declarative (autobiographical) structures*. When recovering or recreating the autobiographical memories of the event, the patient should be encouraged to relay those memories that have the highest probability of eliciting intrusive symptoms, such as flashbacks or physical sensations. Because the sensory-perceptual representations of the memories in the brain are accompanied by intense emotional reactions, a high emotional involvement is necessary for therapy.

Consistent with this view, Jaycox (1998) showed that treatment success in exposure therapy is positively correlated with the level of fear initially experienced in treatment, that is, the higher the level of fear experienced initially, the greater the success of the treatment. The task of a therapist is therefore to encourage the activation of painful memories and to prevent the patient's habitual strategies of avoiding or ending the activation. At the same time, the therapist should assist the patient in organizing the declarative or autobiographic memories related to the traumatic event and in placing the event in time and space. *Habituation* of the emotional response occurs as the memories are no longer capable of eliciting the response part of the fear network. As habituation takes place, the telling of the memories will no longer evoke strong emotional reactions, confusion, and fear in the patient.

Associations between stimuli and fear responses cannot always be erased in therapy of PTSD patients. For certain individuals there may always be some fear that is evoked upon remembering the event. Instead of attempting to extinguish all fear through habituation, new associations with the stimuli may need to be established. In this case, the new association would be the declarative or factual knowledge that is constructed and tied to the stimuli that provokes intrusive symptoms. For instance, a goal for a victim whose fear is activated by the sight of fire might be to associate some declarative knowledge with the sight of fire, such as the time of day or time of year, rather than the emotional content of the memory. Several repetitions of the new associations may be necessary before the declarative knowledge is the preferred representation that gets activated when reminded of the event. Only after these associations are firmly established will the fear responses and the associated intrusive symptoms be inhibited by the new knowledge base.

### 2.3.3 Speechlessness of Trauma: Sociopolitical Implications

In addition to the known fact that psychological trauma is a consequence or outcome of violence, there is also increasing discussion as to whether this psychological trauma can contribute to the number of violent conflicts and wars in the world. Organizations that provide psychosocial interventions in war-affected societies have justified their interventions not only as a means of improving mental health care for individuals, but also by making the case that these intervention are relevant to society and on a political scale. One common assertion is that the treatment of so-called *traumatized societies* is necessary to break the *cycle of trauma* (Tauber 2003; UNICEF, 2001). The cycle of trauma argument implies that victims of violence are more likely to become perpetrators later on. At the same time, treatment of traumatized survivors is considered to facilitate forgivingness and reconciliation within the society.

Whereas it is unclear to what extent and how political processes affect the mental health of victims, it is very likely that the psychological status of victims has an effect on social and political processes beyond the assumed cycle of trauma. In every society there are individuals who want to speak out about what has happened and to pass their experiences on to their children as well as to the public. Some of them will be able to do so on their own, and many local human rights groups have evolved to give these people a forum. Many survivors of the Holocaust have chosen to document their own experiences as a means of educating subsequent generations (Frankl, 1946; Bettelheim, 1986).

A considerable number of people, especially those who suffer from PTSD, are unable to narrate their personal histories because of the pathological effects of the traumatic events on their memory. This puts the victims at a disadvantage in comparison to the perpetrators and bystanders who usually have no difficulties explaining their position. Offering victims a means of processing their traumatic events and documenting their history can help to give them a voice within their society. During the Pinochet regime in Chile, Lira, and Weinstein (published under the pseudonyms Cienfuegos & Monelli, 1983) developed *testimony therapy* as a specialized treatment approach for torture victims, which directly addresses this issue.

Testimony therapy is an innovative approach that combines political as well as psychological goals. The biography of the survivor of human rights violations

| Summary      Treatment of PTSD |
| --- |
| Utilizing memory theory of PTSD, the main goal of therapy is to construct a consistent declarative (autobiographical) representation of the sequence of events experienced by the patient. The act of creating this coherent narrative enables the patient to be exposed to a sensory image of the events. This process allows for habituation and reduces fear responses over time. The task of a therapist is to encourage the activation of painful memories and to prevent the patient's learned strategies of avoiding or ending the activation of these memories and physical sensations. At the same time, the therapist should assist the patient in reorganizing the memories related to the traumatic event and in allowing the patient to place the events in time and space. The visualizing or imagining of the events is necessary for the patient to reconstruct his or her life story and will stimulate the learning that these memories are not life-threatening. The patient will habituate in the process and will become accustomed to remembering the events without activating strong emotional responses. |

is documented in detail with an emphasis on the persecution history and traumatic events experienced. The resulting documents have been used to accuse the regime of human rights violations and, as a whole, have become a powerful tool in the resistance to the Pinochet dictatorship. Thus, this treatment approach serves two distinct purposes: on the one hand, it serves as a method for facilitating the emotional processing of the victim's traumatic event, resulting in improved mental health, and, at the same time, it acts as a document which can be directly used for political purposes. Other therapists have followed this example and used testimony therapy for different groups of survivors of wars and torture (Agger, 1990; Weine, 1998). Despite these reports offering promising results for treatment, testimony therapy has not been widely used in mainstream psychosocial organizations, which primarily favor non-political approaches, such as supportive counseling.

## 2.4   Narrative Exposure Therapy (NET) – The Theoretical Model

### 2.4.1   Rationale of NET

In contrast to the considerable body of PTSD treatment research in western settings, knowledge of effective treatment of PTSD in populations of civilians affected by war is still scarce. Notwithstanding the considerable attention war-torn populations have received from psychosocial organizations in recent years, very little clinical research has been conducted on how to adequately support and treat these groups.

The majority of survivors of war and torture are unable to safely escape their countries, forced instead to flee to insecure places within their home country or in adjacent regions that are often equally affected by war and terror. In addition to living with violence, many of these refugees are also living in poverty, suffering from malnourishment, and are dependent on humanitarian aid. It seems plausible that these living conditions would question the applicability of any psychotherapeutic treatment. However, experience shows that this is not the case. Contrary to Maslow's hierarchy of needs, suggesting that treatment for psychological problems cannot be addressed as long as the basic needs of nutrition and safety are pressing, our investigations show that survivors see their mental health as having the highest priority and that mental functioning is the prerequisite for self-efficacy and meeting one's basic needs. Difficulties with mental and daily functioning, which constitute a part of a clinical diagnosis, in turn hinder autarkic living (national economic self sufficiency) as well as social and economical reconstruction and development. Healing from PTSD thus empowers survivors to live self-determined lives.

Given the large numbers of people and limited monetary resources in refugee camps and settlements, any psychotherapeutic intervention must be brief. Broad scale treatment programs must be pragmatic and easy for local personnel to learn, even with little or no access to medical or psychological education or additional training. Consequently, the method must be adaptable to multiple cultural environments and easily implemented. The oral tradition is a common element among many cultures, thus narrative approaches, such as NET, seem ideally suited to cross-cultural applications.

Narrative exposure therapy (NET) is an intervention that was developed for the treatment of PTSD resulting from organized violence. Given the vital need of a standardized short-term approach, we have developed NET based on principles of cognitive behavioral exposure therapy and testimony therapy (Neuner, Schauer, Elbert, & Roth, 2002, Neuner et al., 2004a). For NET, the classical form of exposure therapy was adapted to meet the needs of clinically traumatized survivors of war and torture. In exposure therapy, the patient is requested to repeatedly talk about the worst traumatic event in detail while re-experiencing all emotions, bodily sensations, and implicit memory parts associated with this event, but this time in a safe and protected environment. In the process, NET weaves *hot implicit memories* into the story unfolded by *cool declarative memories* allowing the majority of patients to undergo habituation of the emotional response to the traumatic memory, which consequently leads to a remission of the anxiety disorder.

Pure exposure methods usually work with the worst event, i.e., the one traumatic event a person has experienced, assuming that this will lead to the best treatment outcome. However, most victims of organized violence, war, and torture have experienced several traumatic events, and it is often impossible to identify the worst event before treatment. To overcome this difficulty, NET uses the chronicity of *testimony therapy*: Instead of defining a single event as a target in therapy, the patient constructs a narration of his whole life, following the timeline of his life from birth to the present while focusing on the detailed report of the traumatic experiences.

**Summary   Basic Principles of NET**

Narrative Exposure Therapy (NET) is a treatment approach that was developed for the treatment of PTSD resulting from organized violence. NET was developed by vivo as a standardized short-term approach based on the principles of cognitive behavioral exposure therapy and testimony therapy by adapting it to meet the needs of traumatized survivors of war and torture. In NET, the patient repeatedly talks about the worst traumatic event in detail while re-experiencing the emotions associated with this event. In the process, the patient constructs a narration of his life, focusing on the detailed report of the traumatic experiences. The majority of persons habituate and lose the emotional response to the traumatic memory, which consequently leads to a remission of PTSD symptoms.

## 2.4.2 Elements of NET

The focus of NET is twofold. As with exposure therapy, one goal is to reduce the symptoms of PTSD by confronting the patient with memories of the traumatic event. However, recent theories of PTSD and emotional processing suggest that habituation of the emotional responses is only one of the mechanisms that improve symptoms. Other theories suggest that the distortion of the explicit autobiographical memory of traumatic events leads to a fragmented or inconsistent telling of the narrative of traumatic memories (Ehlers & Clark, 2000). Thus, a second element, the reconstruction of autobiographical memory and a consistent narrative, also should be used in conjunction with exposure therapy.

As a prerequisite for the induction of emotional processing, memory traces are reactivated and the whole fear-structure gets engaged:
a) Emotional episodes are coded in memory as networks of mutually activating information units. According to Lang, when processing the network, activity in one unit is transmitted to adjacent units, and depending on the strength of activation, the entire structure may be engaged (Lang, 1977, 1993).
b) Reactivating an old, consolidated memory trace renders it vulnerable once again, much as a new memory would be. The literature shows that a previously acquired (conditioned) fear memory can get influenced and disrupted when it was properly reactivated before (Nader et al., 2000).

Experience in use of NET with patients has led us to the assumption that patients are not always able to estimate the degree to which the "hot memories" are problematic in an individual's life or even the content that is encapsulated in these hot memories, especially when the memories are being remembered or recreated outside the context of the whole life story. However, patients may be able to identify these same elements when presented with the task of facing the memories within the context of an autobiographical exploration. Dori Laub and his group at the Archive for Holocaust Testimonies at Yale University reported the following experience:

> ..when the first testimony began, everything fell into place, because the power of the testimony silenced all differences. Everyone in the room was transported to another time and place, a setting that had been waiting untouched and unchanged for many years behind locked doors. No one, including the witnesses themselves, knew beforehand what the testimonies would contain; experiences and reflections came out from recesses of memory that the witnesses did not even know they had.
>
> Dori Laub, "Fortunoff Video," Archive for Holocaust Testimonies at Yale University (personal communication)

People with PTSD often fail to integrate traumatic experiences into the narrative of their lives. As said before, the survivor often cannot report the related experience in a consistent, chronological order and thus this person has no explicit link between the various events, life experiences, and the context within which the events occurred. By using NET we are able to carefully step forward through the complete biography of our patients' lives in chronological order. In telling the story, the patient is exposed to the sensory information that accompanies the memory and to the image of the events themselves. The patient actually triggers his or her own fear network in the telling by narrating the fragments throughout the course of therapy and he or she is able to reweave the events back into a *cool-system framework* controlling the triggers present with the hot memories. As a result, the accompanying anxiety, which evolved from the strangeness of dissociative fragments, is defused. All somatosensory percepts (physical sensations), cognitions (thoughts), and emotions relevant to the fear network and involved in the traumatic sequences of memory will be comprehensively uncovered in detail as the narrative unfolds. The course of events is established (in time and place), labeled and transferred into speech until a meaningful and consistent narrative is reached. All traumatic events are revisited until their horrifying impact dissolves.

NET focuses on both the habituation of emotional responses to the memories of the traumatic events and on the construction of a detailed narrative of the events and their consequences.

---

**Summary     Elements of NET**

What are the therapeutic elements of NET that have proven effective in trauma treatment?

1. Active chronological reconstruction of the autobiographical/episodic memory.

2. Prolonged exposure to the "hot spots" and full activation of the fear memory in order to modify the emotional network (i.e., learning to separate the traumatic memory from the conditioned emotional response and understanding triggers as cues, which are just temporarily associated) through detailed narration and imagination of the traumatic event.

3. Meaningful linkage and integration of psychophysiological and somatosensory responses to one's time, space, and life context (i.e., comprehension of the original context of acquisition and the re-emergence of the conditioned responses in later life).

4. Cognitive re-evaluation of behavior and patterns (i.e., cognitive distortions, automatic thoughts, beliefs, responses), as well as re-interpretation of the meaning-content through re-processing of negative, fearful and traumatic events – completion and closure.

5. Regaining of one's dignity through satisfaction of the need for acknowledgement through the explicit human rights orientation of "testifying."

# 3 The Therapeutic Approach of NET

## 3.1 The Basic Procedure of Narrative Exposure Therapy (NET)

Within a relatively small number of sessions, the patient constructs a detailed and consistent narration of his biography in cooperation with the therapist. The focus of the therapy lies on the completion and integration of the initial fragments of the traumatic events into a whole, including the sensory, emotional, and cognitive experiences of the incident. The testimony is written down and, depending on the willingness of the patient, used for documentary purposes. This procedure has been adapted to the special demands of refugees and has evolved to the following standard:

The first step is to conduct an assessment of the individual's mental health status, including a diagnostic evaluation of PTSD. Following this evaluation, a psychoeducational introduction is presented to the survivor, focusing on the explanation of his or her disturbance and symptoms, as well as a statement about the universality of human rights. This is followed by a preparatory introduction to the therapeutic approach. Treatment starts immediately following the initial diagnostic assessment, which also includes collecting demographic data, completing a medical and psychiatric history, and assessing for current complaints.

A typical refugee narrative extends over the following topics:
- Personal background and individual history prior to the first traumatic event or persecution.
- Experiences from the beginning of persecution to the first terrifying event.
- Terrifying events.
- History of flight.
- Life in the refugee camp.
- Plans, hopes, and fears concerning the future

The first, a pre-trauma period of the therapy may be used as the time during which a foundation for the process is laid and a good rapport between therapist and patient is established. This time also serves as a tutorial for both therapist and patient. In the beginning it is very important that the patient and therapist feel comfortable communicating with each other, so that the patient understands what is actually expected from him or her in terms of how the process of telling the life events will proceed. Also, during this time, the therapist is able to become familiar with the individual expressions and unique characteristics of the patient. In this warm-up phase, for example, the telling of emotional, warm, or exciting moments in the patient's early life offer themselves as a training ground of sorts for emotional processing and communication between patient and therapist.

During the telling of the events in the following phases, the therapist structures the topics and helps to clarify ambiguous descriptions. The therapist assumes an empathic and accepting role. Inconsistencies in the patient's report are gently pointed out and often resolved by raising in-depth awareness about recurring bodily sensations or thoughts. The patient is encouraged to describe the traumatic events in as much detail as possible and to reveal the emotions and perceptions experienced at that moment. The patient is assured that he or she is in full control of the procedure at all times and will not be asked to do anything against his or her will. A translator, oriented beforehand to the psychological goals, may be necessary.

During the session, the therapist writes down the patient's narration or the translation. In the subse-

| Summary | Basic elements of NET |
|---|---|

A. Construction of a consistent narrative of the patient's biography.
B. The therapist supports the mental reliving of the events that the patient will go through and the emotional processing that goes along with this. The therapist assists the patient in creating a chronological structure of the initial fragments. The therapist assumes an empathic and accepting stance.
C. The therapist writes down the survivor's testimony. In the subsequent session, the material is read to the patient, who is then asked to correct it or add missing details. The procedure is repeated across sessions until a final version of the patient's biography is reached.
D. In the last session, the survivor, the translator, and the therapist sign the written testimony.
E. The survivor keeps the narrative of his life-story. As an eye-witness report, it may serve as a document for human rights' violations.

quent session, this report is read to the patient, or simultaneously translated by the interpreter if necessary, and the patient is asked to correct it or to add any additional details that may have been missed. The procedure is repeated in subsequent sessions until a final version of the patient's biography is created.

In the last session, this document is read again out loud to the patient. The patient, the translator, and the therapist sign the written narration. One copy of the signed document is handed to the patient; another is kept for scientific purposes, if needed. With the agreement or request of the patient, another copy may be passed on to human rights organizations as documentation of these events. The document may be used for advocacy purposes or published in some other way, if it can be assured that no harm may result for the patient.

## 3.2 The NET Process Step by Step

### 3.2.1 Organization of Sessions

NET is a short-term treatment approach that has been tested with varying lengths of treatment. The number of sessions required depends on the setting and the severity of PTSD in your patient. Initial experience implementing NET in an African refugee settlement indicated that the minimum number of sessions required is four. For the treatment of survivors of torture, more sessions (typically 8 to 12) may be necessary. Ideally, the number of NET sessions should be determined before treatment. This is useful as an open-ended length of treatment may lead to an increase in avoidance. The patient inevitably may avoid discussing the most difficult situations and may prolong recovery and pain indefinitely. On the other hand, if the patient knows that chances to recollect his story are limited, the process avoidance will be overcome more easily and the period of suffering, including the duration of fear (of the session that enters the major hotspot) is limited.

Many patients with PTSD also suffer from comorbid disorders (depression, other anxiety disorders). These associated disorders sometimes, but not always, do disappear with NET treatment. Then, an extended treatment that includes other specialized cognitive behavioral techniques might be necessary after the NET module. In these cases, we recommend starting with the NET, as many comorbid symptoms can be the consequence of trauma and PTSD and thus already be modified through NET.

---

**A general guideline for the organization of sessions can be outlined as follows:**

**Session 1:** Diagnosis and psychoeducation.

**Session 2:** Start of the narration beginning at birth continuing through to the first traumatic event.

**Session 3 and subsequent sessions:** Rereading of the narrative collected in previous sessions. Continuing the narration of subsequent life and traumatic events.

**Final session:** Rereading and signing of the whole document.

---

### 3.2.2  First Session

#### *Introduction*

The therapist starts the first session in the following way:
a) Introduces him or herself (name, profession).
b) Explains his or her interests (the purpose of the present project/mission).
c) Explains the ethical stance.

The patient has a right to know who the therapist is and what his or her motivations are. This initial phase and the way the therapist presents him- or herself and his/her work, is already a crucial trust-building step between therapist and patient.

> **Example:**
> My name is ... I am a psychologist (nurse, social worker) from the organization ... (NGO, university, school). I am here to assist people who have experienced extremely stressful conditions such as war (rape, forced migration, torture, massacre, accidents) and to document the human rights violations that have taken place. I usually work at vivo's outpatient clinic... (in a treatment center, in a hospital) with refugees from many different countries. We hope to use what we learn from you to improve the way refugees are supported and respected in the future.

Always invite and encourage the patient to ask any additional questions he or she might have.

### Pre-Treatment Diagnostics

Since this manual deals with the treatment of PTSD rather than how to diagnose PTSD, we will not go into detail on clinical interviewing in this manual. (Respective training material on how to apply a PTSD diagnostic interview has been prepared by vivo for various project countries.) It is evident, however, that establishing a clear psychiatric history and correctly diagnosing PTSD with the use of a structured interview requires extensive theoretical and practical training and skills.

---

**A short overview on some of the currently useful diagnostic instruments for PTSD:**

Some currently used instruments that have been developed to measure psychiatric disorders and PTSD:

**CIDI** – Composite International Diagnostic Interview (section M, interview & diagnosis according to DSM IV und ICD-10; developed by WHO)

**CAPS** - Clinician Administered PTSD Scale (interview & diagnosis according to DSM-IV; also measures severity and intensity)

**SKID** – Structured Clinical Interview for Mental Health (PTSD interview & diagnosis according to DSM-IV)

**PDS** – Post-Traumatic Stress Diagnostic Scale (Self report measure filled out by the patient; measures the frequency and occurrence of PTSD symptoms)

**UCLA PTSD Index for DSM IV** (Self-report; child, adolescent and parent version; measures frequency and occurrence of PTSD symptoms; diagnosis according to DSM-IV)

---

To ensure whether an individual has PTSD or not, it is not sufficient to rely on a self-report instrument. A structured interview by an expert is mandatory. It is important to not just measure the occurrence of PTSD symptoms, but also the quality, frequency and intensity of these symptoms. It is necessary for the therapist to have a good, reliable sense of the individual's condition and complaints. Since we know that many PTSD patients also suffer from comorbid disorders, commonly occurring conditions, such as depression and drug addiction, should be screened for as well. While depression may reside with NET treatment,

drugs are often self-ascribed as a means not to think about the events and, as such, hinder processing of the memory as required by NET.

PTSD diagnosis always includes an event checklist that screens for typical traumatic event types. Such an instrument provides the therapist with an overview of the traumatic history of the patients, and what events might appear within the narratives.

When introducing the preliminary assessment to the patient, explain that you have brought a set of questions with you, which will ask about symptoms that many survivors often suffer from. Explain it is necessary to gather this information in order to get a better idea of what the person is experiencing and that it will help you to establish a diagnosis. You should also be sure to mention that while some items may apply, others may not. Before you start the interview ensure that the person has understood the importance of answering each question. Finally reassure the patient that all answers given will remain confidential.

If the presenting patient does not meet the criteria for PTSD, it is necessary to decide what treatment modalities, other than NET, are available to help the person with his trauma. NET, so far, was only evaluated for patients who meet the criteria of PTSD.

### Psychoeducation

After the initial interview and diagnostic assessment, the respondent will be interested in learning the results. If the person suffers from PTSD, it is advisable to continue with psychoeducation immediately following the diagnosis. Initial patient education includes explaining the patient's condition such that he or she understands the diagnosis. It is important to explain to the patient that trauma symptoms are a common response to extreme and harmful experiences and that violence causes not only injuries to the body, but also to the mind and the soul. Most people suffering from PTSD symptoms feel relieved when they hear that there is a well-defined concept for their condition, that they are not "losing their mind" (as they might fear themselves), and that these wounds to the soul can be healed, although scars may be left.

Continuing with the psychoeducational component, explain to the patient that the symptoms, although a common response under such horrifying experiences are not serving a useful purpose and are only leading to continued suffering. Explain that memories of the trauma are intrusive occurrences, which may come in the form of visual images, single sensory perceptions, or other more complex internal states, into the mind and body. Explain that these intrusions keep the person in a state of vigilance as long as the trauma is unresolved. The unprocessed material thus requires conscious processing, which will occur within the therapy. Once the incidence is successfully filed or stored in memory as part of the complete personal biography of the patient, the symptoms will decrease.

---

**Psychoeducation should entail elements of the following:**

- **Normalization** (it is normal/understandable to have such reactions after a trauma)

- **Legitimization** ("symptoms" experienced today are the result of responses from the traumatic situation)

- **Description of trauma reactions** (including related symptoms)

- **Explanation of the therapeutic procedure** (imaginative exposure & habituation, narration, and a step-by-step explanation of the therapeutic process)

---

1. Psychoeducational example of *Normalization:*

*Anyone would be distressed after what you have experienced. This aftershock is known as a post-traumatic reaction. The human brain is designed to promote survival. Therefore, our mind and body are made in such a way that they will perceive and store threatening information to a great degree. Because this happened to you, your body is in a state of looking for and predicting danger before it occurs again. It is far preferable for us vulnerable humans to be too cautious, too hyper-vigilant. However, this is a survival strategy which is painful and extremely exhausting, as you know. It is no longer needed now.*

2. Psychoeducational example of *Legitimization:*

*The problems you are experiencing now are not adaptive responses. In a life-threatening situation people become over-aroused (no sleeping), danger-focused (not concentrate on other things), and numb (not feeling any pain of your body). During the event, your body and mind were in such an alarm mode (e.g., sweating, heart pounding, rapid respiration). This is a common state for your body to be in following a traumatic event. [use the particular symptoms of the survivor to explain]*

3. Psychoeducational example of explaining the symptoms – *intrusions, hyperarousal, avoidance:*

*No matter how hard survivors try to avoid them, the memories always come back. They enter into your everyday life, both at night and during the day. All of a sudden you may get upset, anxious, or detached from reality without knowing why. During a terribly horrifying moment, your mind cannot comprehend what is going on. It is just too much. You are overwhelmed by the bodily alarm reaction and anxiety. You are very aroused in order to react fast and ensure survival, but you have no time in these moments to process any of this information. However, your brain has a completion tendency: It brings up these feelings and fragments later in order to understand and digest and put together all of this, until it makes sense. Reliving those feelings, pictures, and bodily sensations indicates that the mind is actively attempting to process this horrible event, to make it understandable – because this may be vital throughout life. It causes these unresolved inconsistencies to re-emerge into consciousness again and again. But, you push them away each time, because they are so painful and horrifying. You avoid them. What you want to do is now to give them room here during therapy. We want to explore them together and eventually give your mind a chance to understand and integrate these memory fragments.*

During the course of narration it is vital to show and verbalize your empathy and respect for the person and the tragic experience that has been lived through. Stress the wonder that the victim has managed to survive or that, e.g., she or he was able to save the children. Make this part brief but personal. Only mention positive things you truly believe in. Don't exaggerate. The patient might be struggling with survival guilt and belaboring this could exacerbate the negative feelings. If you make him/her a hero he/she might not dare to tell you about the event for which he/she feels guilty or ashamed. The patient may end up hiding events from you. The therapist must not judge or evaluate the particular behaviors that led to survival.

It is advisable to work out your own way of explaining the theory behind NET to your patient according to the culture, age, education, experience, and world-views of the individual patient. It is preferable to stick to the theoretical part of this manual. Children will need a unsophisticated but equally full explanation. It might be good to provide psychoeducation to children in the presence of their caretakers, so that questions can be addressed at the same time. Treatment, on the other hand, is often easier when relatives are not present.

Regardless of the type of patient education model being used, the main elements should result in the following:
• The patient should clearly understand what you are going to do and that he or she has voluntarily agreed to participate.
• The patient should understand what is expected of him or her in the process of NET.
• The patient should not be left with unanswered questions about the therapeutic activities and the techniques you are employing.

Most people do not have any experience with psycho-therapy; some people may never even have heard of it. However, there is usually a concept of healer, elder, or counselor within every culture. It is very important to explain that this *healing journey* will only be possible when the patient is fully active in the process and fully aware of the procedure. The patient should understand that this is not a passive act performed by the therapist onto the patient. It is important to explain the possibility of an elevated fear level during the exposure process – these are moments the survivor has successfully avoided so far. Psychoeducation should answer questions like: Why is the patient willing to seek treatment now? How can talking about the traumatic event help this person to overcome their suffering? Why is giving a testimony an important step in the healing process? These are questions the therapist may pose to the patient in moments of doubt or confusion.

4. Psychoeducational example of *Explaining the interaction of avoidance, exposure, & testimony:*

*This terrible experience left you with a wound that cannot heal properly. It has been hurting and bothering you ever since it happened. Just like an inflammation, every time you touch the past experience, it hurts. Therefore, as you quickly learned, it is better not to be in touch with these memories of the past. However, when a surgeon cuts the wound and removes the infected tissue, it has the chance to heal. Some people would like the same*

*thing done with their traumatic wound, and they ask us for anesthesia. Unfortunately, this is not possible. In order to alleviate the pain from this wound you must stay conscious and expose yourself to the memory of the traumatic events by re-weaving those fragments back into your story and into your biography. When this is successfully completed, the symptoms will subside.*

*In order to successfully integrate the terrible things that have happened to you, we need to gain access to theses past events. We want to look at all the thoughts, feelings, and bodily sensations you experienced during the incident. We want to explore them as completely as possible and go through the incident in slow motion.*

*I know that you have tried hard ever since to erase these feelings. They have been terrorizing you and leading a life of their own within you. However, we do not want them to do this to you any more. At this time, we are going to face them together. Up until know, it may have felt as if you have been held captive by them. This is often exactly what the perpetrators wanted. They want that you will remain a prisoner of these horrible events forever. But we are not going to let this go on. We are going to do something about it. If you can manage to vividly remember those memories, feelings, and sensations you had during the incident of the event long enough, those terrible emotional reactions will eventually subside. They will lose their grip and the impact they are having on you. They will fade away...I know it is hard to imagine, but I will help you and this can become true for you, as it has for many others.*

*What has happened to you is a violation of your human rights. Our ethical standing is based on the Universal Declaration of Human Rights, where the international community has agreed on your right to have a dignified life. Nobody is allowed to violate or harm you. Through the process of giving testimony about what has happened to you, we would like to provide the chance for you to do justice through the documentation of what you saw and went through. Testimonies like this counteract forgetfulness, ignorance, and denial.[1] (Your report will be furnished in a written form and, depending on your wish and accep-*

---

1 Dori Laub, child survivor, Clincal Professor of Psychiatry at Yale University and Fortunoff Video Archive for Holocaust Testinmonies at Yale, (personal communication).

*tance, can be used for documentary purposes and human rights work. However, the story of your suffering will be kept absolutely confidential if that is what you want.)*

5. Psychoeducational example of *Explaining the narration procedure:*

*Through telling your story, we want to construct a detailed, comprehensive, and meaningful narrative of the traumatic events in your life. The goal of having you retell the things that have happened to you is so that you can reintegrate it into your and your people's life history. We want to fill in all the gaps and holes until your testimony is complete. We want you to retell it to us until some of the bad feelings about the events subside, until some of the pain dissolves, and until the fear has a chance to defuse. In our experience, the more complete the narrative, the more the symptoms will get better. We will always go according to your life's timeline. We will proceed in chronological order, step by step, as the events unfold. After this, we will go over it again, correcting and completing things, as necessary, until we reach a final version within 4– 6 sessions. However, each single session will always be taken to a point of completion. It will last about 60–90 minutes. We will take enough time at the end of each session to make sure you are comfortable with whatever came up during our work.*

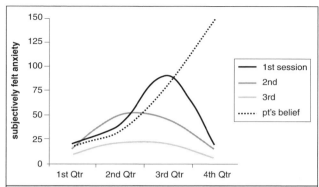

**Figure 4.** Change in subjectively felt anxiety across sessions: During the first session, the patient typically believes that fear and anxiety will increase indefinitively. Explain that it will be like crossing a mountain, whereby a plateau will be reached, after which the fear subsides. The next time the mountain will be much lower, i.e., the anxiety level will climb less each time the narration is repeated and elements are added.
A session must not be ended before the subjective and physiological arousal has subsided.

It is mandatory that you tell your patient clearly that it is common to experience fear and high arousal when recalling the traumatic event during narration (Figure 4). Explain that the severity of the reaction to the traumatic incident is unknown until the memory has been retrieved. There may very well be surprises. It is part of the therapeutic work to uncover exactly how the trauma network is connected and which experiences are keystones in the brain's network. Reassure your patient that sessions are always taken to a point of completion and that whatever has been triggered in a session will be worked through to a point until the patient is comfortable again. Inform him/her that information processing may well continue even after the session has ended. There might even be a transition phase during which symptoms become worse. Reassure your patients that during the whole therapeutic procedure you will always be there. They must know you will always be there to turn to when difficult feelings arise in the session. In subsequent sessions, the therapist should always ask about what the patient experienced between sessions and these topics should be addressed, as needed, in that session.

Do not forget to tell the person that nothing will be the same again once this process has started. Our experience is that, as a result of the therapy, survivors will begin to feel different, think different, take action or change their way of behaving – possibly even during the course of therapy. In addition, NET might have consequences on the social network as well. As therapy survivors begin to dare to stand up for their rights, they often want to speak out. They rank and respect their own needs and conditions more sensitively, they refuse to tolerate abusive relationships, and some may even want to change their lifestyles. Yet regardless of whether any of this happens, exposure therapy is a personally very challenging intervention. While in treatment, patients need a warm, supportive, and understanding environment. During some sessions the patient may require a particularly supportive social network. These times are usually during the second session (when the individual is first talking about the trauma), the third session (when the person is approaching and intensely working on the "hot spot") and the forth session (when the person is beginning to process and integrate the difficult memories).

### 3.2.3 Second Session

#### *Preparation for the Narrative*

After a diagnosis of PTSD has been established by diagnostic interview in the first session, and psychoeducation has been provided, the narration can begin (Figure 5). This is usually during the second session. Once again, you should begin the session by briefly explaining what you are going to do together and by giving a clear timeframe to your work.

You may ask your patient at this time if she or he has any remaining questions. Beware, however, that this may open the door to avoidance. Your patient might use question-asking as a way of avoiding rising fear and of delaying recall of the events. At the same time patients are extremely tense, since they know that "It is going to happen today". They usually want to get the process over with as quickly as possible. For this reason, it is advisable to not waste too much time getting started. Help your patient get started by asking the question, "So, when/where were you born?"

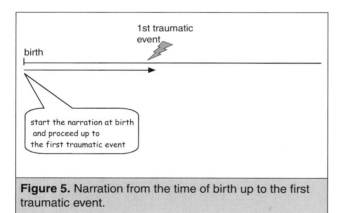

**Figure 5.** Narration from the time of birth up to the first traumatic event.

### Starting the Narration

The chronology of the narration should address all traumatic incidents throughout the course of the person's biography. This will likely proceed through the following stages: childhood – pre-trauma – first traumatic incident – post-trauma – lifetime in between – second and following traumatic incidents – outlook for the future.

Start the person's narration with their family background. Get a picture of how the patient grew up, what the relationship to his parents was like, and what other significant persons played a role in his life. Even during the pre-trauma period it is advisable not only to collect the facts, but also to encourage emotional processing. When the individual is narrating some event that was particularly pleasant or some minor stressful event, the individual can begin to practice processing the emotional content. Children par-

ticularly enjoy talking about happy times, but adults will also enjoy talking about joyful moments of their childhood. For many people who have been exposed to organized violence and war, the memory of good moments in their life have disappeared altogether with the bad memories. This exercise in bringing up emotional content can be useful in training the patient to chronologically narrate an event. The patient can learn to include emotional as well as cognitive and physiological details. Try to get a feeling as to how these various experiences shaped the person's unique way of coping with stressful events, as this might help to understand the patient's reaction on the traumatic events. You might ask yourself the question: "Who" was this particular person when trauma struck?

The time you spend on the pre-trauma period depends on the number of sessions that are available for treatment, the number of traumatic events in the patient's life, and on life period in which the first traumatic event occurred. If this event took place in childhood, the amount of time you can spend talking about life before the event will be relatively short. However, do not spend too much time on this period prior to the event. The patient has been psychologically preparing to talk about the trauma, and some survivors become impatient when too much time is spent talking about other things. On the other hand, some victims may attempt to extend the discussion of pre-trauma so as to avoid discussing the difficult material. As a rule of thumb, there are two possibilities: 1) You spend about 30 minutes on the pre-trauma period, reserving enough time to discuss the first traumatic event during this first 1–2 hour session, or 2) You spend a whole first 45 min narrating session on the pre-trauma period and do not discuss the first traumatic event at all. Regardless of which option you choose, never spend more than one session on the pre-trauma period.

### Narrative Exposure to a Traumatic Event

In this next portion of the manual, the NET procedure will be explained in detail. Each step is the same for every traumatic event the person has experienced. (See example of a complete narration in Appendix B)

### Recognizing a Traumatic Event

One of the important steps about gathering the information from the narrative is developing the ability to recognize when the patient is discussing a traumatic event. There are different pieces of information that can be helpful in determining what is a traumatic event in the narration. As a first step, you can always rely on the information you gathered in your pre-treatment diagnosis. The individual identified those events that were most traumatic in her lifetime. Use this diagnostic information as a tool, making sure to read over these forms before beginning the sessions. By being aware in advance of what the person experienced, you can be listening for clues that the patient is broaching difficult topics.

Another way of identifying when the patient is discussing a traumatic event is by the way that a person is speaking. Often, during NET, the way a person talks will change when they have been asked about a difficult time period or are coming to the point of discussing a traumatic event. These are some cues to look for:

a) *The person's report may begin to be more fragmented and incoherent.* When the thoughts are fragmented or incoherent, you might have difficulties understanding what the person is trying to tell you about that time period. Sometimes a traumatic event might even be completely skipped or left out of the narration. However, oftentimes the patient will drop a subtle hint about the trauma while attempting to avoid it or having difficulty expressing it. For example, a patient might say: "Then, in 1998, the war came to our town. I lost my brother, we had to flee". If a patient gives this type of vague description with missing details, you should always ask for more information. In this case, you might ask the patient if he/she personally witnessed how his/her brother was dying or if there were moments at that time when his/her own life was in danger.

b) *You may observe that the patient gets nervous and emotional.* When the patient becomes nervous or emotional the narration may be interrupted. This may be due to intrusive memories that are coming to the individual's mind. The person may appear to be mentally absent or may be making general comments about his life rather than continuing with the narration. Be aware of the possibility of passive (dissociative) and active avoidance. If you notice this type of behavior, either absence or escaping, ask the patient if traumatic memories have come to mind. If the patient admits to experiencing difficult memories, and if these memories correspond to events from the time period in the narrative being told, then it is important to continue with the narration.

Once you have noticed that your client is approaching a traumatic event, then the major work of narrative exposure begins. Be aware that narrating a traumatic event will always take some time (at least 40–60 minutes) and that you should never interrupt this process. Only continue with this part of the narration when there is enough time left in this session to fully discuss it.

### Assessing the Context of the Traumatic Event

When you get close to discussing a traumatic event, *clarify the period just before the incident* in order to enable the patient to embed it into the greater life story. The therapist must never work on the incident as a fragment of the person's life. It is key at this moment to orient the events and the speaker to time and place. Ask questions such as: "Where were you living at that time?" or "What time of the year/day/season was it when that happened?" "Were you already married at that time?" After getting a general sense of the time and place, then try and pinpoint the event even more precisely by determining the day.

> The following contextual information must be clearly narrated before you talk about the event in detail:
>
> - **Time and setting:** Establish *when* the incident took place. Time of the year, time of the day, particular moment in the day.
>
> - **Location and activity:** Establish *where* the incident took place. Where was the person at that time? *What* was s/he doing?
>
> - **Beginning:** Establish the beginning of the incident. What point *marks the beginning* of this trauma or experience?

### Starting to Narrate in Slow Motion

At this stage, the process of narration slows down. The therapist shifts to *slow motion* in time. Your patient's tendency will probably be to speed up even more and to jump to events further in the future. For this reason, it is going to take some persistence to keep the patient on a slower track. On the part of the patient it is going to take some courage to slow down the recall of the event. At this point, even more experienced trauma therapists begin to feel nervous and may want to avoid the difficult content and the increased signs of suffering of the patient. Learning to recognize this impulse will be helpful for the therapist, as it becomes an indicator that treatment is going well and that the patient is on the right track.

---

At this point in time, make sure to:

- have survivor *imagine the beginning of the incident*. Begin to work through the incident from this point of the patient's imagination, viewing all of it in sequence.

- go in *slow-motion!*

- help the patient to *focus on what was being perceived* during the traumatic incident (physical sensations, thoughts, actions at the time – ask for shape and color of objects, types of smell, patterns of sounds etc.). Support the processing of the material by following the emotional reactivity. Generate the physiology of that emotion: Pursue memorial association of the affect and generate memorial cues that elicit the physiologic responsiveness.

- *reinforce reality*. Prevent avoidance, dissociation, or flashbacks. Make sure that the person stays with you in her/his consciousness in the present time and talks *about* the past

- not allow the patient to be taken back completely to the past in the form of a flashback. *Keep the patient grounded in the present.*

---

Place the incident within the context of the rest of the day. If, for instance, the traumatic event being described happened in the afternoon, start by asking questions about the morning on that particular day. Ask questions like: "Do you remember what you were doing that morning?" "Who was there?" "How did you feel?" "Was there anything special about this day?" "What did you do next?" As you get closer to the traumatic moment, go more and more slowly, i.e., have more details reported.

As you get close to the time of the incident, ask questions that pertain specifically to the minutes and seconds prior to the incident. For instance: "So, you were sitting in front of the house with the fallen roof?" "You were walking on the right side of the gravel road at the time?" Help the patient to focus on those details that can be remembered. Again, sensory information

is very important. Descriptions of sensory information include: "I am aware of harvesting in the back part of the garden," "I was picking beans that I put in a wooden bucket," "I could smell the yellow flowers," "I saw the sun going down behind the village," or "I was busy thinking about my baby." Focus on the point that marked the beginning of the traumatic events. For example, the patient may say, "I smelled something burning" or "I heard a scream and my sister was running towards the house" "It was suddenly very dark." Try to awake sensory memories. Ask your patient to place himself at the beginning of the incident and to start going through the incident from that point, viewing all of it in sequence.

---

**Example – The beginning of the traumatic experience**

It happened at the end of the rainy season in that year. My son was 2 years old then. We lived on the South side of the village of N.... close to the mountains. My husband was working in town at that time. I was in the house cooking that afternoon. I prepared cassava. It was hot inside and I felt a bit tired. My cousin, who had been visiting me, had just left. We had been talking about water problems. All of a sudden I could hear shooting outside. (narration continues ...)

*The next part of this incident happened outside of the village. The therapist again establishes the circumstances before the patient will be asked to place herself at the beginning of the sequence:*

It was already dark, after sunset. I was running together with my son in the middle of the road. I am aware that my hands were too sweaty, that I could hardly hold my little boy. Even now when I tell you about it, my hands get wet. (narration continues ...)

---

### Narrating the "Hot" Memory

The essence of NET is to connect the hot memory, i.e., sensations, feelings, and thoughts to the corresponding sequences in the autobiography by putting all memory fragments into words and thus into declarative memory.

None of the processes by themselves are effective. It is not enough to let the patient just feel and reenact the traumatic experience without maintaining good chronological order within the narration. On the other hand, a good narration without an activation of all the

The main procedure of emotional exposure within NET consists of two processes that must be present simultaneously:
(1) The hot memory (the fear structure) must be activated.
(2) The elements of the fear structure need to be put into words and to be inserted in the narration about the traumatic event.

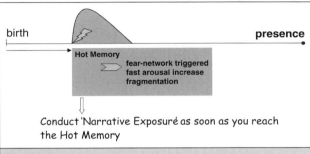

birth                                                          **presence**

Hot Memory
⇒  fear-network triggered
fast arousal increase
fragmentation

Conduct 'Narrative Exposuré as soon as you reach the Hot Memory

**Figure 6.** Upon reaching the traumatic event, the patient's "hot memory" is triggered.

elements of the fear structure, i.e., without emotional involvement, is also not helpful. It is important to be aware of both processes and to have the ability to switch between the two interventions and to support both elements. The NET process can be best understood as a spiral, which winds up towards the goal of a comprehensive, meaningful narrative of the traumatic incident.

Be mindful of the following elements when encouraging the narrative process:

Narrating – Re-experiencing in greater depth – Labeling in more detail – Integrating into the narrative again – Further narrating – Continuing this sequence

### Interventions Used to Activate and Label Hot Memories

The survivor might find many ways to avoid being exposed to the frightful experiences again. In these instances, the therapist must be both empathic and persistent while being able to hear the worst of events without fear. Some patients may immediately begin to demonstrate noticeable symptoms of high arousal (sweating, trembling, heart beat), whereas other patients may be able to avoid any emotional involvement and stay surprisingly cool and calm. In both cases, the intervention is the same. The therapist is to ask questions about the contents of the fear structure.

Be aware that *hot memory* – the fear structure – consists of many levels: sensory, cognitive, emotional, and physiological elements. The activation of one single element or level can easily lead to the activation of other elements or levels. The therapist should be cognizant of addressing the fear structure on all levels. It is helpful if the therapist also imagines the traumatic situation in order to determine what might be salient elements. If, for example, a person saw grotesque scenes, like mutilated bodies, it is most probable that the visual details of these scenes are a key sensory element of the fear structure. The therapist should ask for a detailed description of these images, even though the patient (and maybe the therapist as well) would like to avoid this. Keep in mind that if the images are in the fear structure, the patient sees these pictures in the form of intrusions anyway. It is crucial to try and help the patient put these images into words before they are given the opportunity to avoid them.

There are two types of interventions that help in activating elements of the fear structure:

1. *Direct questions*
   With direct questions, the therapist can simply ask questions that address the elements of the fear structure across the different levels. There are two ways to do this, either in terms of the past or in terms of the present tense. The therapist might begin by asking the questions in the past, such as "What and how exactly did you feel when the gun was in your back?". However, when hot memories are activated, the individual often experiences the events as if they were happening in the present. In this case, the therapist may shift techniques and refocus the events of the present into the past. For example, if a patient experiences a strong sensation in the present, which is most likely related to a hot memory, then the therapist is to relate it to the past. These sensations should never be left as part of the present. For example, if a patient reports that he feels a strong pain right now, ask him if it is exactly the same pain he felt during the traumatic event. This will help him to understand how his current experience was shaped by the traumatic event.

2. *Feedback of Observation*
   Some elements of hot memory – especially its expression in physiological and also behavioral responses – can be observed by the therapist. Direct feedback can be given about an observation like, "I can see your hands are trembling," or "Your eyes are tearing up now." This will allow the patient to become more aware of these sensations and will

**Table 3.** Example questions used to target elements of the fear structure across different levels of processing

| Element of fear structure | Past | Present |
|---|---|---|
| Sensory | "What did the mutilated body look like?" "Could you smell the dead bodies?" "Could you hear the others screaming?" "Could you feel the gun in your back?" "Did you feel the pain in your legs?" | "Do you have the pictures of the mutilated bodies in your mind right now like it was then? What can you see?" "Can you see the soldier right now like he was then? What does he look like?" "Can you smell the dead bodies right now like you could smell then?" "Do you feel the gun in your back right now like you felt then?" "Can you feel the pain in your legs right now like it hurt then? How does it feel?" |
| Cognitive | "Did you think that you would die at this moment?" | "What did you think then, what now?" |
| Emotional | "Did you feel intense horror at that moment?" | "Can you feel the horror right now, like it felt then?" |
| Physiological | "Did your heart beat fast at that moment?" "Did you sweat a lot at that time?" | "Can you feel your heart beating fast right know, like it was beating then?" "Are your hands sweating right now, like they were sweating then?" |

lead to further activation of the elements of the fear structure. The therapist must not be afraid of feelings the patient verbalizes, of obvious physiological arousal, or of any behavior at any stage, as it reassures the patient that the therapist is accompanying him/her closely. There is no need for hesitation about attempting to label the patient's responses: experience shows that the patient will inform the therapist immediately, if the feelings have been labeled incorrectly.

The only thing that the therapist does with the sensations described by the patient is to help put them into words and fit them into the narrative. The therapist might invite the patient to perceive his or her own emotions without judging. This may be difficult for the person at first as s/he may still feel guilt or shame. The therapist shall be a model for this process by listening to the patient's experiences without judging.

It is important to trust the process of habituation. This continuous process of experiencing hot memory, while putting the elements into words and into a coherent narration will lead to habituation. Through this process the emotional impact of the sensations and the physiological arousal will decrease. Initially, some emotions might be difficult to accept, like rage, worthlessness,

and guilt. However, the moment of exposure is the moment to experience the fear intensely. Therapist should not be sidetracked by the patient into a discussion about the adequacy or correctness of these emotions. This is not the time for cognitive interventions.

### Interventions to Narrate

One way to monitor the therapist's own attentiveness to the storytelling is to try and imagine if a good movie could be made from the patient's descriptions. The patient's recall and explanations should be so detailed that it is possible to get a clear picture of what happened throughout the story. For the therapist, it is a good idea to try and keep this little film playing in one's mind. Most likely there will be gaps and inconsistencies in the narrative, which will become more noticeable when it is difficult to imagine what was taking place in the "film." At these times, it is the therapist's job to interrupt and intervene immediately. The therapist may want to say something like "Maybe we can stop here for a moment. I am having trouble understanding what is going on in this sequence." Additionally, the therapist may try repeating as much of the story as she knows to the client followed by: "…and what happened then?". These interventions will help the patient to construct a

**Table 4.** Example of what sensory re-experiencing and labeling of emotional states may look like. In this case, the example of staying in touch with the perceptions is more important than the actual story.

Preceding this interaction is continuous narration up to the following crucial moment:

**Patient:** "... And then I was climbing that tree my brother sat on."
(Therapist can see, that the patient's knees are trembling)
**Therapist:** "How do your legs feel right now, when you imagine the climbing?"
**Patient:** (astonished, looks towards the legs:) "Well, the muscles are shaking a little in fact ... and my heart is beating fast...I feel somehow weak."
**Therapist:** "You are getting excited ...?"
**Patient:** "Yes, I think it is because I know what is coming next. I had to climb higher up to get to my brother."
**Therapist:** "Your body remembers the climbing?"
**Patient:** "I have to do it ...but I am so afraid of falling...even more for myself, than for him ..."
(Therapist realizes that the hands of the patient form a fist)
**Therapist:** "Can you feel the texture of the bark where your hands touch the wood?"
**Patient:** "Oh, my hands are sweaty, even now. I am afraid they won't make a firm hold! And this smell .. this is exactly the smell that reminds me of this situation again and again, each spring time ..."
**Therapist:** "Ok ... carry on climbing now as you did then."
**Patient:** Silence
**Therapist:** "What happens?"
**Patient:** "I don't know ... I don't remember ...I am confused."
**Therapist:** "Maybe your body knows? What do you feel?"

**Patient:** "I am shaking...I should save my brother, but I can't...Oh, no, it is like in a daze, I can't see any more..."
**Therapist:** "What did you see then, when you were in the tree?"
**Patient:** "I can see the leaves and the shade and the head and the arms of my brother hanging down from the tree. I see his face and I know that he can't hold on for much longer ... His face is stained ... His hands are clinging to the branch...I don't dare move."
(Therapist realizes that the patient is "freezing")
**Therapist:** "How does your body feel right now, when you remember this immobility?"
**Patient:** (takes time to get to the present feeling) "I feel helpless and my body is paralyzed ..."
**Therapist:** "Where?"
**Patient:** (focusing on his perceptions) "Only the arms, oh my arms ... I can feel them again ...Look, they are trembling and my legs too ...It makes me so sad that I couldn't help ... (crying) ..."

Therapist comforts the patient as he cries. The patient now has overcome the immobility state. He is "de-freezing" from paralysis and numbness. The emotions are perceivable and are labeled. The person narrates the end of the scene with the help of the therapist. In the next session, he will start to explore more details of the event, placing himself at the beginning and going through it again. He will integrate them into the existing narrative of what actually happened then, how he feels about it, and what he thinks about it today.

detailed narration and show her/him that s/he is not alone in re-experiencing this process.

When the first hot spot is being discussed by the patient, the therapist might prefer to stop transcribing the narrative. It will likely take all the attention of the therapist's focus to handle the emotions and simultaneously keeping the narration going. As soon as there has been some habituation, the therapist may resume writing. The therapist might also recite aloud to the client what he has written down and understood at this time. Be sure to always use the survivor's own words and idiomatic expressions.

### Interruptions Through Strong Sensations

Sometimes the narration is interrupted because the person experiences somatic re-enactment and soma-

tosensory intrusions, or intense bodily sensations, which s/he cannot understand or link to any event in that moment. Instead of talking about fear, it is important to stay with the sensory elements. You should assist the patient in getting in touch with the somatic experience and give the patient the opportunity to find out what the feeling means or the source of the feeling. When the narration is caught in a hot memory, the therapeutic measure is to help the person become aware of what is happening and to help the patient sort through these perceptions. The therapist will help the patient trust her reactions and experiences, which might be confusing and seem to lack sense.

The first step is to identify the sensation. The therapist would assist with questions like:
- "What does this sensation feel like?"
- "Where in your body do you feel what?"

- "What quality does the sensation have (cold, warm, fast, slow, heavy)?"

From there, the therapist will help the person categorize these perceptions and integrate them into the narrative. In order to build up the patient's trust in her own inner feelings, the therapist will gently, but unwaveringly, proceed and reinforce the person, in whatever way s/he chooses, to get into contact with her/his sensations. The therapist will assure the person that whatever appears is perfectly all right and that there is no need to analyze or judge it. All of this can be done later on. Perceiving and describing the sensations are the priorities.

> **Example How focusing on perceptions "tells" the trauma story**
>
> A man, who was witnessing a massacre, interrupts his narrative at one point. He had been bending forward in his chair for quite a while. Because he had been sitting like this for a while, he then noticed that his back was hurting. As he became aware of this sensation, he also noticed that he was experiencing a feeling of suffocation as well. In response to the therapist's question, "Where do you feel it?" the patient suddenly commented, "It is in the neck…and my heart is beating fast." The therapist encouraged the man to continuing becoming aware of the perceptions and sensations of his body. Describing it more carefully, he mentions that it is very dark around him. The man begins to get very excited and his body stiffens. He is hardly breathing. A few minutes later, still continuing to observe and name the sensations of his body, he realizes that the different elements of sensory information that he is experiencing come together to form a whole picture. It is a part of a traumatic scene that he lived through. The man was in panic during a traumatic incident, in which he anticipated getting killed if the persecutors found him. He was hiding for hours squeezed in a dark hole, completely focused on whether there were any footsteps coming closer. Now all of these body reactions made sense: a fast beating heart, being unable to breathe properly, a sensation of narrowness and darkness. The experience was then semantically integrated into the narrative, by putting words and meaning to the experience and to his bodily sensations. Other parts of his PTSD-related experiences, such as nightmares of being trapped in a cave, were also meaningfully connected to the scene.

## Habituation

*For a more in-depth discussion of this topic, please see the checklist for therapeutic detections to support emotional processing and habituation in Chapter 4. Challenging moments of the therapeutic process – NET in-depth – There is no habituation*

Habituation is the decrease in symptoms that occurs after being exposed to the stressor for a significant amount of time. The continuous process of activating and narrating hot memory will lead to habituation, which means that the emotional impact and physiological arousal decreases over time. A session should never be stopped before some habituation has taken place. In fact, there has been evidence that ending a session, when the emotion is still at its peak level of intensity, only serves to aggravate the symptoms (Rothbaum & Foa, 1992). Consequently, the length of time that the patient is exposed to the recall of a hot memory must be long enough to allow the trauma to lose its emotional intensity. The arousal peak, or that highest level of emotional intensity around telling the event, must have been reached and a notable reduction in fear and excitement must have been present before a session should be ended.

Figure 7 shows a successful and typical habituation process of an exposure procedure as felt subjectively by the patient and as can be measured with physiological indicators.

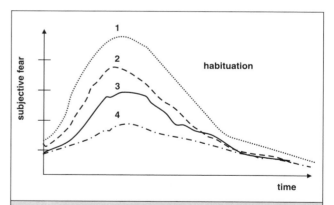

**Figure 7.** During the first emotional exposure, patients might have the perception that fear will increase infinitely. Initially (1), fear will go up until it reaches a peak and decreases naturally. After a second (2), third (3), and fourth (4) emotional exposure, fear will decrease significantly and habituation settles in. When exposure is stopped while fear increases, e.g., by avoidance, before habituation can take place, a negative pattern of increased anxiety is likely.

After habituation takes place, hot memory is transmuted into cool memory. However, full habituation cannot be expected after only one single session. Some fear reduction will take place within a single session as the patient is exposed to the traumatic life events in the telling of these events. As the habituation process takes place, the client's high level of arousal, originally experienced while addressing the hot memory, will come down from its highest point. Further habituation will take place in following sessions, when the events are reviewed again. Habituation will continue to take place between sessions, as the patient will most likely continue to think about the event differently than before treatment. By the final NET session, the goal is to achieve the maximum level of habituation possible.

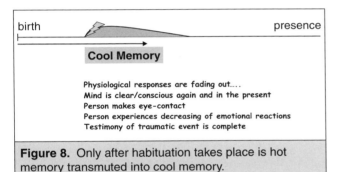

**Figure 8.** Only after habituation takes place is hot memory transmuted into cool memory.

NOTE: The biggest mistake at the point of elevating fear response during exposure would be to halt, interrupt, or avoid discussing the memory before habituation (or a feeling of relief) has occurred. During "exposure," arousal and negative emotions are going up. During "closure," arousal is decreasing, the therapist supports calming down. Always be unambiguous in which direction you are going: **no mixture of exposure and closure**!

### The Period Just after the Event Narration – Ending a Session

After the arousal has been reduced noticeably, be sure to bring the narrative to a close for this session. Even if time in the session is running out, it is of utmost importance to establish a clear ending to the traumatic event that has been worked on. The rule is: **Never end a session with your patient in the middle of recovering a traumatic scene!** The way to bring this closure is by moving on to the event that occurred immediately after the event. To do this, the therapist tries to have the patient verbalize in at least a few sentences

what happened in the time period following the incident. It is important to clarify the time period, whether it is in minutes, hours, or days, following the traumatic event, in order to enable the patient to integrate the incident into the greater life-story. The therapist might use questions such as the following: "When did it end?" "Where were you?" "What were you doing?" "What did you feel?" "Who was with you?" "What were they doing?" "What were your expectations at the time?"

The therapist thus begins with story telling prior to the trauma, and proceeds to events occurring during the trauma and shortly after the trauma. This allows for the trauma to be placed within a context of time and space and allows for the patient to grasp and sense the context surrounding the event. Before actually ending a session, the therapist will assess to determine whether the patient's arousal level has subsided and be certain that the person is calm again with a peaceful, positive, and relaxed feeling.

We can make sure of this by looking for the following signs (adapted from Bisbey & Bisbey, 1998):

* *The patient's emotional state is improved*: return of normal face color, the patient is demonstrating and making statements that he feels better (relieved, peaceful, smiling); muscle tension and trembling has resided; the body position indicates a more relaxed internal state; and negative physical sensations have disappeared (pain, headache).

* *The patient's attention shifts from his or her mental environment to an awareness of external environment.* The person is making eye contact with the therapist; is noticing things in the environment; is aware of the passage of time; is aware of external noises; is feeling hungry. The patient may be commenting on activities that s/he will be involved in after the session or the patient may be commenting on things s/he is noticing about the therapist.

* *There is evidence of a cognitive shift in the patient.* The patient's thinking about the meaning of the traumatic experience seems to have changed. The patient states that s/he has achieved insight into the experience; the patient is making connections between the trauma and other experiences in her/his life; the patient is reporting that her/his experience makes more sense now. The patient talks about the meaning of the event. Finally the patient reports that it feels as if the trauma is over and is no longer as significant as it was.

This work should bring you to the end of your session. The length of a session depends on the person being treated. There are no fixed time frames for the length of sessions. Although the therapist may want to cover as much ground as possible, it is important to be sensitive to what an individual can process in any given time. Usually a session finds its natural ending within about 1 1/2 hours. Finish a session when it makes contextual sense (for example, after you have worked through a chapter of the biography) and based on the patient's process in the session. This is better than setting an artificial time. The best moment to "fade out" a therapeutic session is when there is enough emotional distance from the last exciting and arousing hot memory. Never start working on a new hot spot when there is not enough time to complete the process of exposure and habituation.

### Cognitive Restructuring and the Days After

At the end of a session, after some habituation has taken place, patients often use this "cooling-off period" to make sense of the trauma and to put meaning to the trauma. More formally, one would want to support this so-called *cognitive restructuring* process. The following issues often arise after exposure to the memory of the events:

- The patient might have some *new insights about the meaning of the event* for her/his life. Often patients realize how the everyday emotions and unhealthy behavioral patterns (such as general anxiety, mistrust, rage, outbursts of anger) have their origins in the traumatic event.

- The detailed narration often leads to a *more thorough understanding of a person's behavior during the event*. This might help to modify resulting feelings of guilt and shame, as the person might realize that she had no other choice at that time.

The next logical step would seem to be comparing the once hot memory to the now cool memory and discussing the implications of this transition with the patient. However, this step can be postponed by the patient until the beginning of the next session. Many survivors need time to realize the impact of an exposure session. A good part of the cognitive processing and emotional evaluating happens after the exposure session – without the presence of a therapist. Much of the beneficial process of increased awareness of what has happened takes place between sessions. When the therapist and patient meet again, the therapist should be open to positively receiving any thoughts and considerations the patient might have had since they last met. The therapist may want to explain to the patient again that this process of coming to new realizations is a natural sign of processing information and is a first step towards a healthy development. If a patient wants to talk about these issues, the therapist can support the process by reinforcing a change to more adaptive beliefs.

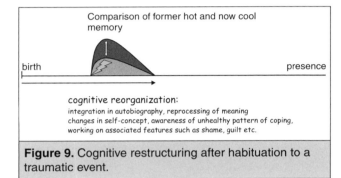

**Figure 9.** Cognitive restructuring after habituation to a traumatic event.

If the survivor brings it up, ethical issues or human rights topics can be addressed with the survivor. Subjects such as regaining one's dignity or potential actions that might be taken, such as political involvement, may very well arise. The patient may also bring up other topics related to healing, such as joining a self-help group or seeing some alternative therapist (someone who performs body work, massage, or other alternative practices).

### Scheduling a New Session

Following the first exposure sessions some days might be difficult for your patient. Thoughts or feelings that the person had previously been avoiding may resurface. Anxiety may become a bigger issue to contend with. The individual facing these thoughts or feelings may experience more sleeplessness than usual or may suffer from an increased number of nightmares. The patient might find herself feeling more angry or irritable than normal. It is important to inform the survivor about the possibility that these experiences might take place and it is equally as important to inform the person that this is a completely normal reaction, one that is part of the healing process. Your patient may want to start keeping a diary and or jotting down anything that s/he observes. The life of the person will start changing – not just internally, but also in interactions with others or in day-to-day behaviors.

Because of the intense nature of the work being conducted and the processing that is necessary, sessions should not be scheduled too far apart from each other. Two sessions a week is ideal. Less than that is possible, but some patients might find greater lapses in time difficult to cope with. With clients who have reported severe traumatic incidences at different periods in life, it is particularly important to agree on when the next session will be. This will prevent the avoidance that leads to prolonged suffering. The only exception in terms of a short time between sessions is with the last session. It might be useful to schedule the last session ten days after the next to last session. This intentional break will give the patient time to evaluate and rethink the entire testimony process. In between sessions a lot of cognitive and emotional processes will take place for the patient. Ask your patient to watch out for those processes and possible changes, so that you can start the next session by talking about them. As stated earlier, exposure processes not only occur during, but also between, therapeutic sessions and alter the associations within the fear structure.

### Tenses of the Narrative – The Emotional Impact

While working on the incident during the therapeutic session, the survivor should process the material in an optimal state of arousal. We want the client to get emotionally involved in the controlled re-living of the event. Usually a break-through is achieved, when the person is finally able to feel intensely and when she becomes really emotional about the scene. However, reliving always must be "as if" only: We want the person to process the past emotionally, while being grounded in the present. The person should never be hurled back in the factual scene without keeping a strong bond to reality.

- When under- engaged: use present tense to make the scene more vivid and to get the full activation of the fear network (e.g., "You are lying on the floor right now ... can you feel the hand on your body now? Where do you feel it touching? ...")

- When over-engaged (or panicky): use past tense to achieve a lower level of autonomous activation, reinforce reality and point out that it is over (e.g.,: "take a moment and experience (feel), how you are sitting on this chair now in the room with me here, while we are thinking about that moment in the past, when he had his hand on your ..."

- Explicitly compare *then*- and *now*- responses, sensations, emotions, and cognitions during the session (e.g., "your heart was beating in that moment then, how is it now...?")

The written testimony is always furnished in past tense, while sensations and feelings that are produced by the story are put in present tense.

### Levels of Parallel Processing During NET

There are different processes going on in parallel that need the therapist's continuous monitoring during and between NET sessions:
(1) "The incident:" what happened then, at the time of the incident (past)?
(2) "Here and now:" what happens now during the session?
(3) "Present:" what is going on currently in the life of the patient and how does it influence the therapy?
(4) "The narration and the narrative:" during the session and when updating the testimony
(5) "The therapeutical contact:" how are "we" doing during and between sessions?
(6) "The therapist:" how am "I" doing during and between sessions?
(7) "Cognitive and emotional reorganization:" during and between sessions
(8) "Admin:" timing, appointments etc. during and between sessions

Following all sessions, the therapist's homework is to write a first draft of the patient's life narration up to the point at which the narration stopped.

### 3.2.4 The Following Sessions

When meeting at the beginning of every session, it is important to be observant of the emotional condition the patient is presenting with that day. This will reinforce the certainty in the patient that you are a reliable and attentive companion in this difficult period of life recall. A therapist must not say things like "You are depressed" since this will label a person negatively without actual knowing whether this is true. Be aware that in a helper's position, a therapist has quite some power over a patient's beliefs. It is always better to speak about one's impression, without judging, to use "I-messages," and to verbalize carefully. One way of starting might be to say, "I can see that your hands are trembling." "How have you been since we met last?" or "I notice today that you look tired and exhausted." "Have you had trouble sleeping these past nights?" Or you might address something you notice in the patient: "I can see that you are restless." "Is something making you nervous/bothering you?" or "Could it be that…?" A few minutes at the beginning of the session can be taken to explore and label the emotional state in which the patient finds her-/himself. Of course, once the patient is settled, the narration proceeds. At this point, your focus is on the life-line. Beware that it might be tempting to avoid it and rather talk about other topics that are pertinent, yet off-task, such as how the patient is coping or how the patient is handling daily problems. Avoidance and with it a conspiracy of silence between client and therapist has many subtle faces.

In the second session and every session thereafter, the written narrative from the previous sessions will be re-read to the patient. At this point, the patient will be asked to fully imagine and relive again the incidents with the purpose of correcting and detailing the report. The purpose of this is that the testimony and the habituation process become more and more complete. Reading the document slowly from the very beginning, once again facilitates emotional processing and exposure in the same way as described above until arousal decreases. Ask about changes in your patient's perception. "Did you feel different this time when we talked about the traumatic incident?" "How about your heartbeat? How was that?" "What were you feeling this time?" In this way your patient starts to build up personal awareness about emotional and cognitive changes within her-/himself. When you come to the end of the document, continue exploring the person's life further. Simply proceed along the autobiography. Do not be tempted to return or go backwards in time, but always move forward (remember that you can bring up past issues in the beginning of the next session). During this process, it is possible that a second traumatic event will emerge (Figure 10).

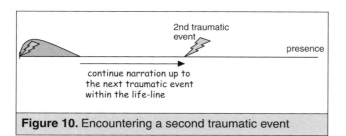

**Figure 10.** Encountering a second traumatic event

By going through this step-by-step process of reading back the narrative to the patient and having the details filled in, an entire narration or eye-witness testimony will be completed, including all traumatic events of that person's life in chronological order (Figure 11).

### 3.2.5  The Last Session

In the last session, the report is read to the patient and all final corrections are made. Again, the therapist must make sure that the criteria for closure are reached. In the final NET session the testimony/narrative should have lost its arousing impact. The patient might look at the narrative with a sense of distance (it's a sad but true story) or s/he might look at it this document as a tool for peace-building or educational purposes. Occasionally, a patient takes the narrative lightly when it is re-read to him, making some comment such as "It's funny listening to my own story… It's hard to imagine that I ever felt like this…" Some may see it as an important personal growth experience.

Finally, the patient, the translator, and the therapist sign the written testimony. The signed document is handed to the patient. If the patient agrees, another copy is kept for scientific documentation purposes. Upon the patient's request, a testimony, in anonymous form, is passed on to a human rights organization for documentation work.

### 3.2.6  Post-Treatment Diagnostic Sessions

Post-treatment diagnosis includes the evaluation of symptoms using the same instruments as prior to the treatment. Ideal times for evaluation are 3 months, 6 months, and 1 year post-treatment. Diagnosis makes little sense earlier than four weeks post-treatment, as symptoms must be taken into account over a period of several weeks. What you would anticipate seeing over time, of course, is symptom remission to a degree where PTSD is no longer diagnosable.

| Summary | Most important rules of the NET Procedure |
|---|---|

- Never stop a NET session (emotional processing during exposure) during the height of fear and anxiety.
- Stay with the patient in the trauma narration until arousal has subsided.
- Prevent de-realization, dissociation, and avoidance
- Prevent the patient from going back and forth in time while narrating.
- Do not mix "exposure" and "closure." The therapist must know which of these separate actions is intended at every moment of the session.

*Exposure* = Fully reliving the events of the trauma scene. Staying in the traumatic incident until arousal and negative emotions subside; habituation is achieved.

*Closure* = Ending the exposure situation and closing the remembrance of the traumatic scene. Supporting the client and helping them calm down until the arousal level has returned to normal.

### 3.2.7 KIDNET: Narrative Exposure Therapy with Children

#### PTSD Treatment for Children

In recent years, a number of investigations from various war zones all over the world have reported moderate to severe rates of Post-traumatic Stress Disorder (PTSD) in children exposed to acts of organized violence and war (see Kinzie et al., 1989, in children from Cambodia; Saigh, 1991, in Lebanese children; Somasundaram, 1993, in Tamil children from Sri Lanka; Dyregrov et al., 2000, in Rwandese children; Thabet & Vostanis, 1999, 2000, in Palestinian children from Gaza; Papageorgiou et al., 2000, in children from Bosnia-Herzegovina; and Karunakara et al., 2004, in Sudanese refugee and Ugandan host children.) Investigations conducted by vivo in Sri Lanka's North Eastern Provinces exemplify the consequences of traumatic experiences and resulting PTSD in children. In an epidemiological survey, in which a representative sample of 420 Tamil school children in the LTTE (Liberation Tigers of Tamil Eelam) controlled Vanni Region of Sri Lanka's North-East were inter-

viewed, vivo found that 92% of the surveyed children had experienced one or more severely traumatizing events, such as being caught in a combat situation, being in a situation of bombing and/or shelling, witnessing the violent death of a loved one, among others. Of those, about a third of the children (29% of the total sample) suffered from severe and chronic PTSD (vivo, 2003), often comorbid with depression and somatization. Just as in adults (Schauer et al., 2003, Neuner et al., 2004), we saw a significant relationship between the number of traumatic events reported and the number of difficulties children reported in social and emotional functioning. Factors such as frequent headaches, sleep disturbance, altered memory function, loss of ability to concentrate and pay attention, decline in school performance, loss of trust, and social withdrawal strongly impacted those children diagnosed with PTSD, limiting their chances for future healthy development.

It is known that heightened stress in childhood accelerates many forms of mental and physical illness. As suggested by studies in humans and clearly demonstrated in animal models, the impact of severe stress during development may leave an indelible imprint on the structure and function of the organism and the brain in particular (McEwen, 2002; Teicher et al., 2002). Besides PTSD, the psychological consequences of traumatic events can lead individuals into social isolation, hostility, depression, and substance abuse, and can foster somatization (Teicher et al., 2002). A significant relationship between childhood trauma and personality disorders, as well as other psychiatric disorders later in life has been postulated.

Research in industrialized countries shows that children and adolescents with PTSD can be effectively treated with trauma-focused cognitive behavioral therapy (CBT). Randomized controlled trials that included children and adolescents in the age range between 3 and 17 years have shown that CBT is superior to non-directive supportive therapy and waiting-list conditions (Pine & Cohen, 2002). In these trials, CBT procedures usually consisted of a combination of cognitive, anxiety-management, and exposure techniques. Child-friendly exposure techniques usually involved narrative procedures, like helping the child to write an account of the traumatic event over the course of several sessions.

The findings from treatment studies in industrial countries cannot easily be transferred to children in war regions or refugee children from other ethnicities.

First of all, most randomized trials have been carried out with children who have experienced sexual or physical abuse. One exception is a study that included children from a resource-poor Latino minority area in Los Angeles who were victims of multiple violations (Stein et al., 2003). In addition, Goenjian et al. (1997) carried out a non-randomized controlled study with early adolescent survivors of the 1988 Armenia earthquake, although the children in both studies can probably not be compared to children from war areas in terms of traumatic exposure and current threat. These trials indicate that standardized CBT including exposure techniques can be effective for children in vulnerable populations from different cultures.

As most children in war areas live in developing countries where resources are scarce, it is necessary to develop a treatment procedure that is easy to learn, short in duration, and can be carried out by trained lay therapists. Current trauma-focused CBT procedures are too complex in this regard. As no conclusive dismantling studies have been carried out so far, it is also unknown what aspects of trauma-focused CBT are responsible for the treatment effect in children. Research with adults indicates that the combination of different procedures does not lead to a better outcome than the single methods alone (Pine & Cohen, 2002). This finding suggests that the concentration on single methods might help to develop less complicated and more pragmatic procedures that are equally effective. Analyzing the requirements of culturally and ecologically sound intervention programs for adolescent victims of war in different cultures, Pynoos and co-workers point to the traumatic experience as the main therapeutic focus in treatment, with a clear recommendation of narrative techniques (Saltzman, Layne, Steinberg, Arslanagic, & Pynoos, 2003).

### Narratives in Children

Current scientific knowledge holds that the ability to narrate one's life story requires abilities, which are not well developed in early childhood. In general, the capacity for autobiographical memory develops with age. Although infants and young children process and retain information (Bauer 1996), events occurring before the age of 2–3 years cannot be recalled in narrative form. Due to developmental limitations, young children are thought to have problems with explicit memory functions. They lack sufficient knowledge to help them understand, as well as make sense of infor-

mation and retrieve higher order memories (Williams & Banyard, 1999).

There is no doubt, however, that even very young children will remember traumatic experiences in an implicit way. It is hypothesized that memories for traumatic events may be encoded differently, partly at somatosensory level, in very small children, as opposed to more exclusively at the verbally-mediated level (Bremner, 1995). On the other hand, due to the presence of threat, traumatic events are usually remembered, even in early childhood, and the memories can be remarkably accurate (Koss, Tromp & Tharan 1995). In very young children (age 2–5 years), who cannot perfectly express themselves in coherent narratives but remember fragments, the memory nevertheless was shown to be accurate and correct (Jones & Krugman 1986; Terr 1988; Howe, Courage & Peterson 1994; Peterson 1996), even when the traumatic event took place a long time ago (Widom & Shepard 1996; Widom & Morris 1997; Wagenaar & Groeneweg 1990). Misperception and forgetting significant aspects of the experienced violence and horror are also common.

However, treatment with memory recovery techniques that involve remembering and talking about the traumatic event and its aftermath was found to improve memory in older children (Goenjian, 1997). An active attempt to help children embed the traumatic experiences into their life context is useful in that it helps the child understand, integrate, and digest these traumatic experiences (Steil, 2000; Tessler & Nelson 1994). In narrative exposure procedures, children are asked to describe what happened to them in great detail, paying attention to what they experienced in terms of what they saw, heard, felt, smelled, the movement they recall, and so on, as well as what they were thinking and feeling at the time. Initially the session is distressing, but if it is long enough to allow habituation, distress falls towards the end and more and more details are recalled; just as in adult therapy. It was shown that after only four sessions of exposure, scores on intrusion and avoidance symptoms dropped dramatically (vivo international, 2003; Yule, 2001). Additional pharmacological drug treatment has not been shown to be beneficial; in fact, drugs might even be harmful to the developing brain (Steil & Straube, 2002).

Even though children from the age of 8 years on are perfectly able to work with narrative exposure techniques, parents and teachers initially report that children would not easily talk about the trauma. Recent experience has shown that many children easily give very graphic accounts of their experiences and are also able to report how distressing it is to live with the related symptoms (vivo international, 2003; Sullivan et al., 1991; Misch et al., 1993). Although child survivors, like adults, experience a need to talk about their experiences, paradoxically they usually find it very difficult to talk with their parents and peers. Often they do not want to upset their caretakers, and so parents may not be aware of the full extent of their children's suffering. Peers may hold back from asking what happened in case they upset the child further; the survivor feels this as a rejection.

Often, however, children's traumatic narratives rely on co-constructions with parents or other adult caretakers helping to complement the story. Co-construction can assist the child in clarifying details of the traumatic experience, understanding its context and meaning, and addressing cognitive confusions (van der Kolk, 1996). Of special note, co-construction can address "pathogenic beliefs" that emerge out of inaccuracies and misattributions. It should be mentioned that parents and teachers are important models and interactive partners throughout the post-traumatic adaptation. However, in forced migrant populations it is likely that the parents have undergone the same traumatic experiences as their children. Therefore, they might bring their own avoidance to the therapeutic process of the child.

In summary, parents' and caretakers' involvement and participation in therapy has been shown to be a predictor for treatment success (Deblinger, 1999; Steil, 2000). It is important to involve children at the right stage of the process and with adequate preparation. In any case, the informed consent that caretakers give to allow child therapy is a good entry point for psychoeducation. It is also necessary and important to respect the child's wishes concerning the parents' degree of involvement in their own narrative process.

| Summary      Children and PTSD |
| --- |
| Children are highly vulnerable to stressors that accompany war and conflict. Many studies show that children emerge from war and organized violence with a number of mental health illnesses and psychosocial problems, including PTSD and depression, whereby both cause reduced daily functioning. The child's right to a healthy intellectual, emotional, and social development is thus denied. |

### KIDNET – Utilizing the Life-Line with Children

Within the last few years, vivo has been developing a child-friendly version of NET, called KIDNET. Clinical trials have been carried out in Uganda with refugee children (Schauer et al, 2004; Onyut et al., in press) and in Sri Lanka with formerly displaced children in the northeast of the country, and under the direction of Martina Ruf at the *Psychological Research and Outpatient Clinic for Refugees* in Germany (url: www.vivo.org⇒ "vivo's outpatient clinic"). One of the key questions currently under investigation is whether or not NET can be applied with equal success to children, as it has been to adults (Neuner et al., 2002, 2004a), and for what age range. KIDNET has been developed by vivo as a child-friendly exposure treatment for children and adolescents with PTSD. (A full KIDNET testimony can be found in the Appendix.)

In our research with children from different cultural backgrounds, ages, and levels of cognitive ability, we have generally been surprised at the extent to which children have been able to explore their life events, feelings, and thoughts associated with trauma. The key element in therapy with children is to gain and deserve the trust of the young patient. Because it is not as easy to gain trust with children simply by talking, as we do with adults, we will often use theatre, illustrative materials, in addition to the life-line exercise during therapy, which involves play and creative media to help children express their experiences. For example, we may encourage children to act out their traumatic experiences in role-play by requesting such actions as "Show me how you sat on the ground when the car came" or by helping them recall details through painting. The therapist might ask, "Can you draw the expression on the man's face?"; "Can you draw a picture for me that shows the house that you lived in and what it looked like?"; or "Maybe you could show me in your picture exactly where the soldier was ..and where you were." These elements are sometimes useful in psychotherapy with adults as well.

Since the life-line exercise is a key feature of KIDNET treatment sessions, it will be described in more detail below. This exercise is especially important for the first NET sessions with a child. It helps to break the ice quickly and employs creative media, which allows the child's life story to unfold in a playful manner. In fact, this simple technique works so well that we have also been able to use it successfully with adults from many different cultures, especially when it is difficult for the person to reconstruct a clear chronological order of his life events.

## The Life-Line Exercise: "Flowers & Stones"

**Figure 12.** Material needed: a long rope, about 10 flower heads, about 10 stones, 2–3 pieces of drawing paper, colorful drawing pens, and a ball point pen

Present the rope to the child. Explain that it symbolizes her/his life with the beginning of the rope marking her/his birth. Ask the child to lay it out on the floor, leaving a good part of the rope unfolded to represent the future. Mark the point of birth and the present. Do not be surprised if the child lays out the life line across the space given or between obstacles. That's okay. Just ensure that it is clearly visible and accessible. Now show the flowers and stones to the child. (Ideally present a mixture of stones and flowers varying in size, color, and shape, to represent larger and smaller life events.) Explain to the child that the flowers represent happy moments in life and the stones stand for difficult, fearful, or painful ones. Ask the child to place the flowers and stones along the life-line. This will take a bit of time. Watch the movements and placements of the child closely. There might also be some backward and forward shifting of objects going on – make a mental note. When the child is finished, start at the time of birth and get an explanation for each flower and each stone that she placed. Make sure that a chronological order is established. Sometimes this means shifting objects around with the child until a proper time line is established. After all major events, both happy and sad, are represented on the life-line, ask the child to make a drawing of this life-line. When she is finished ask her to give a name or a sentence to each flower and stone she has drawn and write down what she says, including a brief note on what event this flower or stone represents. This drawing will serve as an important tool for knowing where the key moments are located in time and space in the child's life. Once you get into the narration, more events, both good or bad (more stones and flowers), might be revealed. That's fine, just ask the child to include them in the life-line drawing. At the end of therapy, you can ask the child to draw the final version of the life-line and to extend the life-line further. Encourage the child to include some plans or hopes for the future. A final drawing can be encouraged in which the child draws her future plans and hopes, such as "'When I get married,' "When I live in a house," "When I become a nurse or a doctor."

Once the life-line has been clearly established, it serves as a road map for both the young patient as well as the therapist. Sessions can be structured far more easily, since you will know where the next big stone, or difficult life event, is hiding. These big stones will take time and energy to explore and they should never be brought up towards the end of a session. The therapist will also know when the happy events occurred in the child's life. These high points are often a good way to finish off a session.

Utilizing these special techniques are just some creative ways of adapting NET for use with children (Figure 13). However, it remains an unresolved challenge as to how aid organizations, active in the field

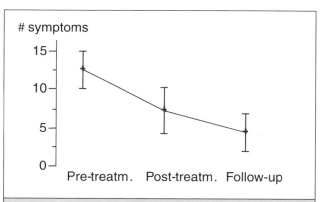

**Figure 13.** The number of symptoms gets significantly reduced in response to KIDNET, as shown by a study of Onyut et al., in press. Note that healing continues in the 6 month between post-testing and follow-up. (Error bars indicated Standard deviations).

of providing mental health services to children, will develop field-friendly tools for this special work. Methods are needed that are practical, can be used in a short-term treatment modality, and which provide effective intervention. Clearly, additional guidelines for the treatment of traumatic stress in child survivors of organized violence and war are warranted and are, as of yet, incomplete.

## 3.3 Challenging Moments In the Therapeutic Process – NET Indepth

There are some typical problems that we face when conducting exposure therapy with survivors of organized violence. These hurdles are rather the rule than the exception. We found it helpful, however, that others have already tried to highlight some of these critical issues (Bisbey & Bisbey, 1998). The following description may serve as an opportunity for a deeper understanding to accomplish the NET procedure.

### 3.3.1 The Patient Attempting to Avoid

Even after careful and sound psychoeducation, it is very likely that a patient may want to avoid this difficult and painful process. As explained earlier, the memory of trauma causes extensive distress to the victim, and so the patient might try to avoid confronting the traumatic material. Avoidance strategies vary from person to person. Some will speed up their narration and lose awareness, others will directly refuse to talk about a subject, others will try to sidetrack to the discussion by changing the subject instead of sticking to the traumatic event. The goal of all of these strategies is to interrupt or avoid the exposure process. Reliving the trauma through imagination, however, is thought to promote habituation. Once habituation begins to occur, the individual will learn that anxiety does not need to remain forever and that avoidance or escape is not necessary to alleviate the anxiety. The therapist, although already having explained this during the psychoeducation phase, may need to explain these mechanisms again if avoidance is occurring (Figure 7). There are two steps to dealing with avoidance: First, you should openly acknowledge the patient's attempt to avoid and validate that the process is painful and that you understand the desire to avoid. Second, you should explain that you are required, as the therapist, to notice and point out when the patient is avoiding. You may then explain that as a team the two of you will work together in close cooperation to prevent avoidance. In some treatments, it may be necessary to intervene in this manner several times.

One reason for avoidance may be that your patient is unsure you will be able to handle hearing her/his story. Most survivors have never had an opportunity to share their story, or have never dared to talk fully about their experiences. This holds true for adults as well as children. It might be important to tell the patient about your own experiences. Tell your patient that you have worked as a researcher, therapist, social worker, nurse, or teacher in the field of counseling, human rights violations, or organized violence, as it applies to you. Share with them that you have worked with refugees, torture victims, survivors, or that you yourself have experienced and overcome war situations or violence, if this is the case. Assure the patient that you know how to assist others in overcoming their suffering. Make sure that you continually demonstrate to the person that you can deal with whatever comes up. This is what you are here for: to accompany the person, side by side, back to the most horrifying moments of her/his past life. People who are afraid of hearing or imagining the atrocities that will invariably arise may fail as therapists in this setting.

### 3.3.2 The Patient Spaces Out: Dissociation and Flashbacks

As explained earlier, some victims may have learned how to disengage from their traumatic emotions, sensations, and cognition. They might have developed unhealthy strategies in order not to feel the pain and threat. The therapeutic challenge with NET is to look at the traumatic past from the present perspective. Reliving does not mean allowing the patient to be taken back to the past, as with a flashback. On the contrary, therapeutic exposure must enable the patient to face past events and to withstand the emotional distress these memories cause to a conscious mind in the present reality. Anything else is not assisting the healing process. Allowing dissociation to happen will only strengthen the avoidance mechanism, increase anxiety, and, in the worst case, integrate the therapist or the therapeutic setting into the fear network. It is of major importance that the therapist helps the patient stay in the present. The therapist will thus promote the patient's contact with their psychophysiological reality. The therapist's job is to make sure the person does not feel overwhelmed while the traumatic memory is activated. The therapist will take care that the patient does not need to escape into a dissociative state marked by freezing, spacing out, or feeling numb.

The therapist must continuously watch out for signs of numbing, freezing, and spacing out. The more the patient is in contact with her/his body and her/his feelings the less likely it is that he will dissociate.

A good indicator for the beginning of a dissociative state is the growing or sudden detachment from the therapeutic contact. The patient's condition may get visibly worse. The person may not respond adequately any more or may not communicate properly. He or she might experience negative phenomena, such as the body stiffening or becoming paralyzed. In these cases, the therapist immediately guides the patient's attention towards the sensory reality. An intervention in such a crisis would be to make the patient more aware of his surroundings in order to help him reconnect with his present external world, by asking questions like "Can you feel the surface of the table in front of you?" or "Do your feet feel warm or cold?"

If these types of questions are not helpful and the patient is experiencing intense pain, de-personalization, or detachment, the therapist might use more direct ways of reconnecting the person with the present. The therapist might attempt to bring in sensory reminders of the current reality by touching the person's hand, for example, or saying the person's name: "Mary, can you hear my voice; can you feel my hand?" The therapist might verbally recognize that s/he knows the patient can hear her/him. "I know you can hear me; it's okay." The therapist should try to tell the patient that s/he is aware of what is going on with them. "Sayid, I know you are far away and having a hard time coming back. I'll stay here with you." The therapist should also try to verbalize whatever the person is doing by making affirming statements that label the patient's behavior, such as, "Yes, you are moving your legs."

If the patient re-experiences the traumatic situation in a flashback, the therapist should provide very clear sensory reminders of the present. The patient should be assured that the threat is over and that s/he is safe in the here and now. Be reassuring and repeat the fact that there is no danger now. In a situation that becomes out of control, such as when a person collapses or has an outburst of anger, it may be necessary to ask a third person to call a helper. Under no circumstances should the patient be left alone.

In case of fainting or collapsing, the therapist should prevent the patient from hurting herself by protecting the head during the fall. The patient should be placed on the ground with the feet elevated. A second person should be called to assist. The therapist should also

lower her-/himself to the ground. S/he will then start to establish a sense of reality for the patient, as described above. The therapist must be prepared for a change in behavior when the patient regains consciousness. The person may be disoriented or confused; or s/he may be very anxious and emotional. Be prepared for any of the above.

In the case a person should collapse repeatedly when exposed to the hot spot (see Neuner et al., 2002, for a case vignette), it is helpful to prevent fainting through increased muscular tension and activation of the emotional system. The therapist should not say to the patient that she should relax just before talking about the traumatic incident; on the contrary, the patient should be encouraged to be excited or engaged in the process. The goal is for the person to stay conscious when exposed to the trauma imagery otherwise the procedure is not beneficial, i.e., building of explicit memory is not possible. Without an excitement of the emotional system, the brain cannot learn that it is possible to be exposed to the memories while staying in the present and the fear network cannot be modified.

### 3.3.3  The Patient Is Withholding Information

In general, when a patient withholds information from the therapist, or chooses not to disclose certain information, the narration cannot proceed, as the patient is distracted from the narrative. The patient's internal attention is alternatively focused on what is NOT being spoken. Patients often withhold information unintentionally. They feel the information is irrelevant or that the information is too confusing to articulate. Things might cross their mind that they dismiss. They assume it is not important to the work being carried out on the traumatic incident or that it is unrelated. Whether this information is relevant will only be determined if the person dares to talk freely about all of their experiences with suffering.

Here are a few examples of why a patient might withhold information:

- The incident happened early in childhood. The person had no cognitive frame or knowledge base to interpret the meaning of these bodily sensations coming from that time period. The adult still experiences the bodily sensations, but as they were not given meaning at the time, the origin of them is unknown.
- The patient is afraid that the information being shared will get back to somebody else, e.g., the partner.

- It is assumed that the therapist might not understand or not accept what she is trying to say.
- In this culture people don't talk about things like that.
- The patient feels some unpleasant arousal, such as a rapid heartbeat, and wants to avoid this feeling.

The therapist might ask any of the following questions to elicit unspoken material:

- "Has anything crossed your mind that you have not mentioned?"
- "Have you thought of something that is difficult to tell me about?"
- "Is there something else you're thinking about right now?"

The patient needs to feel safe enough in the relationship with the therapist to tell her/him whatever crosses her/his mind. If the therapist refrains from judging the patient and from interpreting for the patient, s/he is more likely to feel safe enough to speak frankly. It might be necessary for the therapist to work on safety issues, both exploring the patient's fears and concerns, and providing reassurance and confidentiality of a good therapeutic alliance.

### 3.3.4 The Patient Has Concerns or Pain

If the patient brings up some concern during the session such as "I'm bored," "I have a headache," "I'm too tired to continue," "I have to leave and take care of some business," it might be wise to assume that the client is feeling uncomfortable and is trying to find a method of escape. The first thing a therapist must find out is when during the narration the feeling or discomfort began. The patient's wish to stop the session, to get away from the topic, or to detach might well be part of avoidance.

In addition to what are common or universal biological responses to threat, such as hyperarousal, immobility, freezing, or numbing, patients also might experience during recall specific physical sensations that occurred at the time of the trauma. The patient might feel tense, dreadful, or anxious. Pain might arise in certain parts of the body, especially in the form of headaches. The therapist can come back to the psychoeducational segment in which somatic complaints were discussed. Usually the best tactic is to continue the process of NET until these sensations are defused. The therapist must rely on the therapeutic process in these situations. If the patient feels safe

enough, s/he will be willing to continue through the worst part of the incident until defusing begins, the charge is reduced, and the symptoms subside.

### 3.3.5 There Seems to Be No Habituation

At times, it seems as if the narration has progressed nicely, according to the therapist, yet the arousal level of the patient stays high and habituation has not begun. Usually this is a sign that not all key experiences have been narrated. Something is missing. The following are potentially significant issues that a therapist might focus on in order to detect a missing link.

Here is a checklist for ways to support emotional processing and habituation:

- Check on sensory information contained in the incident. This includes visual images of the incident, somatosensory sensations, olfactory cues (smells), or bodily pains experienced during the incident.
- Focus on what the patient is paying attention to while relating the traumatic event. How much was the patient aware of what was happening in the room? In her own story? In her body? To what extent was she able to pay attention to the sequence of events?
- Check intentions throughout the incident also conflicting or embarrassing ones.
- Check on actions taken during the incident. Did the patient regret having taken certain actions? Were there actions the patient would have liked to have taken but couldn't?
- Look for evidence of the patient's cognitions: thoughts, assumptions, decisions, beliefs, expectations, ideas, and conclusions made during the incident. What did the patient think at the time? What decisions were made? What did s/he believe was going on? What did s/he think was going to happen next?
- Watch for cognitions: thoughts, assumptions, decisions, beliefs, expectations, ideas, and conclusions made since the incident. What does the patient believe about her/his condition? What does s/he think will happen to her/him when s/he has a flashback? What are the assumptions s/he has made about why this happened to her/him?
- Look for "mysteries" in the story. Is there information being given that could not have been available to her/him at the time or since then?
- Observe incongruities in the story line. Look for examples of people or things that should have been present at the time or vice versa, but weren't. Look

for events that should have taken place, but didn't. Listen for events that took place, but shouldn't have.
- Check on practical or existential questions that arise from the incident. What does the client feel about the larger meaning of her/his life? What does it mean in terms of her/his day-to-day life?
- Ask about anything the person wanted to communicate but did not or could not during or after the event.
- Ask about anything the person may have found out about her-/himself as a result of the incident.
- Notice strategies that the patient uses to cope with the incident.

In these instances, the therapist carefully forms her/his own questions to enable the patient to assess material that so far has not been forthcoming. The idea is to recover a missing feature of the incident and to incorporate it into the narrative. The following questions are possible examples. They only make sense in the context of the patient's narration:

- "Was there anything you wanted to *say* at the time of the incident but didn't?"
- "Was there anything you wanted to *do* at the time of the incident and didn't?"
- "Were you aware of anything else going on around you at the time of the incident while you were trying to ...?"
- "Did this experience, at the time of the incident, raise questions for you?"
- "You didn't mention any feelings when you talked about this situation ... Were you experiencing any emotions at the time of the incident?"
- "Did you promise anything to yourself or others at the time of the incident?"
- "How did you react when the man said that at the time of the incident?"

### Summary

Over time, and with each review of the story, the narrative should be improving in terms of content, focus, and de-fragmentation. The narrative should be more comprehensive, complete, detailed, and insightful. The person's level of arousal should be calmer over time. If this is true, there is no need for the therapist to interfere with questions. Commonly, however, the therapist needs to assist in improving de-fragmentation by putting the pieces of the memory-puzzle together. The therapist should be helping to structure the reported elements in time and space.

### 3.3.6  Therapist Avoidance

The therapist should be aware of the behavior s/he might employ unwillingly to protect her-/himself from the horror s/he is listening to. The therapist might build up resistance as a defense mechanism, or she might overidentify and feel sorry for the patient. The first is called joining the *fraternity of non-believers*. This happens when one does not want to shatter one's own deeply rooted beliefs that humans are beings are inherently good or that the world is a safe place. Listening to the survivor's narrative about the cruelty of perpetrators contradicts these beliefs. The second trap is called the *pitfall of sorrow*. This pitfall involves the therapist feeling more sympathy then empathy for the person's emotions. Other authors have stated that denial is a common way for mental health and relief workers to cope with the problems confronted, to reduce cognitive dissonance, and to preserve self-esteem.

De Waal (1988) proposes two forms of denial. The first form of denial involves the therapist's rejection of responsibility. The mental health or relief worker consciously decides not to take responsibility for the suffering of people or for the effectiveness and result of the treatment interventions. As in a major natural disasters, viewing each of hundreds of thousands of people as individuals would paralyze even the most balanced of helper. It would be extremely difficult to feel the impact of suffering for each person as an individual who also feels emotions, who cares deeply family, their country, and their lifestyle (Stearns, 1993). Just as with the survivors themselves, some manner of coping mechanism is necessary to blunt the truth of this realization. The second form of denial is the helper's tendency to incorrectly rationalize away the truth, convincing oneself, for instance, that Africans do not feel pain and death the way that Westerners do, but are used to death and suffering.

As in the example of Africans not feeling pain and death in the same way as Westerners, mental health workers' may use explanations of cultural differences in perception and expression of trauma feelings as a way of coping with the trauma of working with refugees. When faced with the alarming proportion of victim's traumatic experiences, this becomes a form of denial and coping (Stearns 1993). The misconception that traumatic events are not disturbing to refugees can lead to a general de-humanization of refugees (Waldron, 1987). Harrel-Bond (1986) comments on this excuse, saying that there is perhaps no more dramatic way of expressing psychological distance or for denying a common humanity.

Of course, the patient does not benefit from these defense mechanisms employed by the therapist. Survivors are likely to feel emotionally rejected by the therapist. Patients quickly realize the inability of the interviewer to cope with the emotionally shocking facts of the traumatic incident. In order to not harm, overwhelm, or appall the therapist, victims tend to unconsciously minimize their version to a more socially acceptable story. It is the therapist's responsibility to make sure that s/he realizes her/his own mental state and ability to cope. The therapist should receive adequate supervision provided by the team to overcome such mechanisms.

The same is true for the therapist's professional handling of short episodes of emotional outbursts, flashbacks, or brief states of reactive psychosis in the patient. The therapist must not be afraid of such emotions. When painful feelings of the patient find an appropriate way of being expressed in a warm and understanding setting, they will soon come to a natural end. As a rule of thumb, healthy, expressive crying takes about 10–30 min. If it goes on much longer, it may no longer be a healthy expression of grief. Ongoing toneless, soft whimpering is not productive. The therapist will comfort a person who is crying and will facilitate and support the complete expression of sadness and grief. Expression of anger should be even shorter, because it usually is covering some underlying pain that will surface next. The patient should be told that as opposed to rage, anger is a good sign of healthy and strong emotions. It is important to adequately experience and express anger. It is of inherent importance that the anger is cognitively connected back to the feelings that took place during the traumatic scene.

*Note:* The therapist should never push or force the patient to experience some kind of catharsis. As a rule, the therapist tries to match the patient's tone and voice, including the melody and frequency level of the patient, and to stay with the client during the narration. When it comes time to wind down the therapist stays slightly ahead of the patient, leading that process.

### 3.3.7 Memory and Reality

On the journey through the life of a patient, it is important for the therapist to keep in mind that *"memoire"* means reconstruction. The therapist should not expect that the memory of the traumatic events is going to be an exact replication what was seen, heard, or experienced by the person. The therapist should therefore try to imagine the patient's situation at the time of trauma and attempt to understand how the incident is being remembered. The therapist must be particularly aware of the following factors, all of which are known to shape the representation of an event memory (Schacter, 1996; Baddely, 1990; Reviere, 1996):

1. *What were the characteristics of the patient at the time of the event?* How old was the client at the time of the event? What is the gender of the patient? What are the emotional state, physical condition, circumstances of the patient now and at the time of the event?
2. *What knowledge-base did the patient have at the time of the event?* How would the person grasp and understand what had happened to her/him, her/his family, and to other people? How would s/he have been able to integrate this understanding into the existing background and previous experience?
3. *What is the current interpretation of the events?* How does the patient attempt to make sense of the things that happened? Which aspects of the event does s/he connect to others? How are symptoms that arise from the trauma interpreted?
4. *What retrieval strategies does the patient use and what is the context of recall?* In which way does the patient try to remember, the objective facts, the individual emotions and physical sensations, and the thoughts at that time? In what condition is the patient now, during the therapeutic encounter with the event? How does s/he currently feel? What characterizes the therapist's contact to her/him? Does the patient feel safe, anxious, sad?

| Summary | Self-Reflection for the Therapist |
|---|---|

Questions a therapist might pose to her/himself before beginning a trauma-focused work:

- Am I ready to hear this person's story?
- What type of support do I need?
- Am I really convinced that it is beneficial for the survivor to be exposed again to the traumatic memories?
- Do I want to hear it? What about my fear that this story might be horrible to listen to?
- Am I aware of the fact that the survivor probably feels his or her story is incommunicable?
- When and for what do I need peer-support, supervision?
- Am I aware of and how will I handle the two main pitfalls: 1) maintaining a conspiracy of silence and 2) overidentifying with the patient?

Memory can be affected by many things. A memory may be false due to incorrect connections among its elements or due to weak memory traces. Stress or anxiety alter coding strategies and thus affect accuracy and consistency. Memories also change every time they are recalled. During the screening process, the therapist must be aware that certain elements of an event most likely will be fragmentary and or incomplete. The joint work of the therapist and patient will be to restore the whole picture such that it becomes a consistent narration that makes complete sense to the patient.

Sometimes, especially regarding events that happened early in childhood, the patient has intrusive memories but is not sure what happened in the past that created these memory chunks. Some patients wish to recover implicit memories, many of which are presumed to be incidents of childhood sexual abuse. You can agree with the patient to go through the memories with the NET procedure. But make clear to the patient that for childhood events, gaps may remain. The main rule in such a treatment is that the therapist must never be suggestive in regard to what may have happened, and never construct a story that has no clear foundation in the patient's memory. Instead of constructing a false declarative memory (which then will always be in conflict with the implicit knowledge) it is better to help the patient to accept that s/he might not find out if, e.g., the abuse has happened or not.

### 3.3.8 The Therapist-Patient Relationship: Rules of NET and Standard Ethical Principles

First and foremost, the therapist's role is to facilitate and guide the patient's own testimony process while maintaining good, empathic contact with the patient in a non-judgmental way. Here are a few guidelines for this process:

- *The therapist does not interpret for the patient.* The patient is an authority of her/his own experience. Therefore, the therapist does not need to agree with the content of what is being said or the way the patient interprets the experiences. The therapist simply agrees to accept it as the patient's world.
- *The therapist does not judge for the patient.* The therapist must not offend, punish, or invalidate the patient or her/his ideas, perceptions, or actions; nor must s/he praise or validate them. Minor comments, gestures, or facial expressions of the therapist can be a signs of approval or disapproval, which give the impression of judging the patient's performance.

- *The therapist makes sure that s/he comprehends what the patient is saying.* If not, the patient will feel alone and unsupported. In case of confusion, the therapist must seek clarification by admitting not having understood. The therapist might say, "I did not understand what you said. Could you tell me again?" The therapist will empathically encourage the patient to continue with the story and to express her/his feelings. If the patient should waiver or avoid continuing, it is the therapist's task to encourage the patient to continue narrating in a continuous, linear manner along the timeline of that person's life.
- *The therapist does nothing in a session that counteracts the process of narration.* The therapist does not talk about her-/himself, make random comments, give lectures or offer advice. The therapist does not express emotional reactions towards the patient, whether through signs of anger, anxiety, boredom, or inappropriate laughter. When the therapist stays close to the emotional and cognitive processing of the person, s/he is less likely to perceive details that the patient talks about as disgusting, appalling, intolerable, or shocking. If these feelings do arise, it is not appropriate to show these feelings unscrupulously to the patient. On the contrary, a well considered feedback might be helpful for the survivor, who is usually afraid what kind of emotions her/his story might evoke in a listener. It is also not therapeutic for the patient to feel as if s/he must take care of the therapist. A professional therapist is to seek supervision from colleagues when discomfort arises.
- *The therapist acts in a predictable way and with integrity.* This includes educating the patient as to how NET will proceed, what the therapist will do in a session, and what the expectations will be. The therapist will announce and explain when s/he needs to do something that may be unexpected, such as changing seat positions, getting up from the seat, or moving objects in the room.
- *The therapist will always respect the patient's boundaries.* The therapist should never try to work against a patient's will or in the presence of expressed protest. The therapist has to accept the decision of the patient if the person does not want to continue. This does not mean that the therapist has to stop when the patient expresses avoidance. It is the responsibility of the therapist to inform the patient about the consequences of interrupting treatment and the potential benefits of continuing. A clear decision on the part of a well-informed patient must be accepted. The therapist will always respect an individual's physical need for space. If

touching the patient is necessary at any point, get the person's permission, even if you already have discussed the parameters around appropriate touch.

- *The therapist takes complete responsibility for the session, without dominating or overwhelming the survivor.* The therapist will monitor and act on the best interest of the emotional reactions of the patient. In order to allow the patient to put all her/his attention to her/his testimony process, the therapist, similar to a personal secretary or manager who keeps record of the session, keeps the agenda straight and reminds the patient when s/he needs to take the next step. However, allow the patient to take the action. The therapist must ensure that the session is being given in a suitable space and time; and that the environment is as safe, private, quiet, and comfortable as possible in any given situation. Care should be taken not to interrupt a session for any reason. In case of some external interruption, protect your patient from any harm or threat, or from being seen and identified.

- *The therapist must not transfer care to another therapist without preparation.* In some cases, it might be necessary to transfer the care to another therapist. In this case, inform the patient as soon as possible that this will be happening. Build in a transition period, if possible, during which the new therapist will join you for a joint session. Allow for co-therapy to take place long enough for a secure bond to form between the patient and the new therapist. The original therapist will lead the session unless there is some other agreement with the new therapist and the patient. If these steps are not taken, the patient may feel a sense of powerlessness and a lack of control or predictability. Even worse, the patient may feel rejected. The therapist must ensure an environment in which the patient is able to complete the NET procedure successfully.

- *The therapist assures fidelity and confidentiality.* The patient must be absolutely assured that all the information exchanged during the conversation will be treated in a confidential manner. Any written notes will be used only to help reconstruct the experience and to create the written document. The final description will be handed to the patient during the final session. It is then the patient's choice whether this document should be destroyed or preserved and to what extent it should be distributed.

- *The therapist assures the patient that the working relationship will be cooperative.* Tell your patient that you are willing to accompany her/him in the journey through her/his life history. There will be no hierarchy, as there might be in some African cultures and with certain types of faith healing,

such as witchcraft. The person cannot be cured without her cooperation.

- *The therapist is explicit in her/his behavior.* The therapist should inform the patient that there is no such thing as a hidden agenda or manipulative techniques involved. Whatever happens in the sessions will be explained and made explicit beforehand and at any point during the session, if requested.

- *The therapist is responsible for the interpreter.* In many cases interpreters are necessary. Interpreters must be very well trained. The interpreter is bound to all contractual agreements between the patient and the therapist, including confidentiality and ethical principles. The ideal interpreter does not have a "mind of her/his own," but acts as a voice only. The interpreter will need a lot of supervision and professional support from the therapist, since interpreters are often from the same ethnic group as the patient and might have had similar experiences as the patient. Interpreters who show symptoms of traumatic stress must not be employed for translation work.

## 3.4  Limitations of NET

### 3.4.1  General Limitations

During or immediately following the pre-treatment diagnostic session, a decision should be reached regarding whether or not a patient is going to participate in the NET treatment. There are no prerequisites for NET treatment other than the ability to potentially verbally communicate and tell a story about one's life. Children from the age of eight on up should be able to complete this task. There are no limitations with respect to specific knowledge, educational level, or cultural background of the patient. Generally, throughout the NET procedure, the patient should be in good health and her/his basic needs should be satisfied. The patient should be getting an adequate amount of sleep at night and ideally enough food. There should be no current threat, danger, or potential trauma, such as domestic violence.

### 3.4.2  Insufficient Motivation

If motivation on the patient's side proves to be insufficient, NET treatment will obviously not work. Several factors can reduce motivation. These may include fear of reporting, pressure from others (such as a spouse) not to seek outside help, or hopelessness about the potential for relief from these symptoms. The fear of mental health services may also be a factor in that the patient believes a PTSD diagnosis would increase chances for being institutionalized.

### 3.4.3 Medication and Drugs

If the patient currently takes psychoactive medication or abuses substances, NET treatment may not be useful. Drugs may cloud awareness, reduce intellectual capacity, and alter arousal. Preferably the person should neither be on anxiolytic medication nor on sedatives. Excessive alcohol consumption is a problem for the very same reason. The patient should refrain from abusing alcohol during NET. Patients who cannot comply with this request are unlikely to profit from NET.

### 3.4.4 Guilt Feelings

Special caution should be paid to patients who feel guilty and experience intense guilt memories. Survivors of trauma have often been involved in activities that seem intolerable to society under normal conditions. Some survivors feel guilty, even if they were not actively involved in any operation, simply because they are still alive, while others died in the event. This is often termed *survivor guilt*. Survivors may feel unworthy because they were not able to prevent harm from others.

Imagine the loss of children witnessed by a parent. In order to survive or to help others, patients might have had to act against their ethical conviction, their religious moral code, or against the human rights of another person, maybe even leaving another peer or friend to suffer. A survivor may have been put in a position of having to implicate another human being. It may have been necessary to give false evidence, to blame, betray, or humiliate another person, or perhaps even to harm another as s/he her-/himself was harmed. The survivor may not have been able to help others in ways that s/he would have under normal circumstances, either by sharing resources or preventing something terrible from happening to friends or family.

The realization of and confrontation with personal guilt can cause a severe psychological crisis for the victim. Again, guilt is not an exclusion criterion, rather a challenge for the therapist. The therapist should never feel tempted to take away guilt from the survivor, even if it is obvious that s/he is not to be blamed. It is preferable that the patient work through the trauma and hope that cognitive re-structuring post-habituation will alleviate feelings of guilt. Of course, guilt compromises self-worth. As a result, persons suffering from survivor guilt may be suffering from comorbid depression.

# Appendix A: Informed Consent Form

## Informed Consent

Participant's Name: _____

Age: _____ Date of examination _____

Place of examination: _____

Project title: _____

Project investigators: _____

### Explanation of Procedures

I understand that I am being asked to participate in a research study that will explore the effectiveness of therapeutic interventions for reducing symptoms caused by extremely stressful experiences. The treatment approach is called Narrative Exposure Therapy and will require me to create a detailed report of my biography, including traumatic events. With the support of the therapist, I will try to clarify my memories about the traumatic experiences. There will be up to six therapy sessions once or twice a week that will each last around 60–120 minutes. In order to see how helpful this assistance might be, there will be an examination of my symptoms three months after the therapy, after six months, and after one year.

### Risks and Discomforts

I understand that in the course of the treatment the recollections of the traumatic events will be encouraged and may cause personal stress. I understand that the recollections of events that have caused great personal stress may evoke feelings of anxiety and frustration.

### Benefits

I understand that the benefits I will receive from participation in this study include free examinations and treatments that may reduce the intensity and frequency of symptoms that arose from extremely stressful experiences. Participation in this study does not imply any financial benefits.

### Confidentiality

I understand that information gathered during this stuy will be kept strictly confidential. I agree that the results may be published for scientific purposes, provided my identity is not revealed and cannot be reconstructed on the basis of the published data.

### Withdrawal Without Prejudice and Termination

I understand that I am free to withdraw my consent and to discontinue my participation in this project at any time without prejudice against future care. I also understand that my participation in this study may be ended without my consent, if it is determined by the investigators that it is in my best interest or if I significantly fail to follow study procedures.

### Costs to Subject from Participation and Payment and Research-Related Injuries

I understand that there will be no costs for my participation in this study. All examinations and treatments associated with the project will be free. vivo has made no provision for financial compensation in the case of physical or psychological injury resulting from this research.

### Legal Rights

I will receive a copy of this informed consent. I am not waiving any of my legal rights by signing this consent form. My signature indicates that I agree to participate in this study.

*Agreement*

My signature indicates that I have decided to participate, that I have read (or had to me) the information provided above, and that I have received a copy of this consent form.

_____

**Signature of patient (& care taker in the case of children)**

_____

**Signature of therapist**

_____

**Signature of witness**

# Appendix B: Narration of the Life Experiences of Abdul Kadir
(All original names and places have been changed)


## KIDNET by vivo international team Elisabeth Schauer, Verena Ertl & Siyad Bulle, 2003

I was born in M., Somalia in 1990. I have no brothers and sisters. The house of my family was a few miles outside of town. It was a big house and we had a good life. My father was a businessman; he owned a shop. My mother stayed at home. Later I was told that both parents were very happy to have me, since they had waited a long time for a child. I didn't know that. I only felt their love. There are some occasions that I remember clearly: when I was 5 years old we celebrated my birthday with a party at our home. I was very happy then. Later, when I was 6 years old I was taken to school. I was very good at school. I remember that I got a special degree. I was the best in my class. My family and I were very happy and proud because of that. I even remember the date of this special day; it was the 15th of August. During the coming school break, my father took me on a trip around the country to reward me. When we came back we met my mother again at home. My mother bought new clothes for me and I got many presents, like videogames. It was the time of the Idd festival. I had my friends at school. I invited them home. We played together. My father took us out to nice places, like the beach. When I remember this, I wished this life would come back, I was very happy then. When I was 9, my father took me to a city called N. for the 1st time. We were staying in my aunt's home; she used to live there. My aunt was "cool as ice", she liked to be with kids a lot. She also introduced me to other relatives there. She held a big party for me at her place. However, I remember missing my mother a lot. At least we had phone contact during our trip. I was looking forward to go back home to M. But when we came back, the city was in chaos. Fighting was going on. We heard that my mother had to flee the town. I was crying heavily and regretting to have left. But my father calmed me down and assured me that we would be together with my mother soon. I did not know at the time, that I would never see my mother again. We have not found her until today.

Shorty after our return then I went to the market with the house-girl. We wanted to buy some new shoes for me. She was inside a shop. I stood in the street, attracted by shoes in a shop window. Suddenly I heard bullets, there was shooting and panic in the street everywhere around me. People were shouting and running. I can hear the sound of the bullets right now when I remember this, some people were shouting: "Allah Aq'bar," and there was the sound of bullets: "drrrrumm, drrrumm, drrrrumm." I fell down and was crouching close to the ground in the street with my hands over my head to protect myself. A moment later I could feel people running over me. I can feel the pain of their feet on my back right now, how they were stepping on me. My heart is beating fast when I remember this, there is a pain in my back and chest. My head is hurting so much right now. I was injured and in that moment I thought I would die. I started crying. The house-girl must have recognized my voice, she heard me crying. She had been hiding under a roof and when she heard me she ran towards me. She was injured too and crying. She wore only one shoe and was bleeding from her head and mouth. She picked me up from the ground and carried me in her arms. I felt I was safe with her. Her name was Amina, she was about 19 or 20 years old then and very beautiful. She called a taxi, we sat inside and drove away. We were safe in this car and we held each other tightly. I had slung my arms around her and she had her arms closely around me. We were both crying. There was still shooting, running and people crying around us in the street, but I felt safe. As we went out of the city the bullets became fewer. We reached home. My father was there. He held me and hugged me. In that moment all pain was gone, I forgot about all my injuries. All I felt was "I am save now." My father took Amina and me to the hospital. We were treated in the same room, lying on beds next to each other. People were there with aid kits. I had terrible pain in my chest. I was bleeding a lot from the nose. I was coughing blood. I still get the nose bleed now when I remember this day. I also get the pain in my chest and my heart beats fast whenever I remember. I stayed in the hospital for 2 weeks. Then it was time to say goodbye to Amina, I thought we would part only for a few weeks. We sat together for about 30 minutes and said good-bye to each other. When I remember that moment I feel happy and sad at the same time. Happy because she was the best housekeeper I ever had. She was like a sister to me; she cared for me so much. She saved me, even though she had been scared and injured herself. Since that day I have never seen her again. That makes me very sad every time I think of it.

When I came out of hospital I was somehow ok, but still feeling very low. My father took me to my grandma. She was living in a village further away from M. He thought it would be safer for us there. The village was called K. and was not far from the ocean. In K. I made several good friends after some time. I went to Madaras Qu'ran school again.

About one month, after I had moved to the village, I walked around with some friends. By that time the war had nearly reached the village. I wanted to look at the ocean because I liked looking at the water a lot. It always made me calm and happy. My friends went into the forest, so we separated. I went to the ocean alone. When I got to the shore, I stood on a rock and looked down over the water. What I saw was horrible. The water was full of dead bodies up to my feet. At first I had thought people were out swimming. But I realized that there were about 20 floating bodies. They were black, there was blood, most of them were children, about 8 or 9 years old, some women, even pregnant ones with big bellies and a few men. The bodies were floating there with their faces up and the eyes wide open. Their stomachs were already swelling. The moment I saw all these dead bodies I got a shock. I started shouting and crying: "Woowooowoo…!" I was shaking all over, I was frozen there on the rock although all I wanted to do was to run away. I felt intense fear, my heart was racing. I even feel it now, when I talk about this moment.

My friends heard me and came. They took me home. The memory of the street shooting in M. had also come back strongly. My nose started bleeding, I had a terrible headache and the pain in my back, where people had stepped on me came back badly. At home, I got first aid, my father put a piece of cloth on my head and neck. For one week I could not talk, I could not eat, I was in a state of total shock. Then my grandmother managed to calm me down, she explained about life and death to me, she said: "We all have to die one day; when the time comes that God has decided for you, you will die, no matter if there is war or not, that will be your day…". Slowly the confusion in my head cleared up. I became clearer in my thoughts. I started eating and talking again and felt ok. I woke up from that stage, walked around with my friends again and went to school.

At that time I met Halimo, she was a friend of some of my friends. She had heard about what had happened to me. One day she asked me how I was doing now. This was the first time we talked to each other. She was my age and very beautiful, her skin was dark brown. We liked each other instantly. Soon we were spending most of the time together. We were walking around the neighborhood and talking a lot. When I wanted to go running, she went with me. We went to the shops together and she helped me with the housework. She taught me a lot of things and I taught her other things that she did not know. She was like Amina, she cared for me and was kind. We were having a great time. She was so cool. We started giving little gifts to each other. One of them was a postcard that she gave me one day. It read: "Love with all my friendship and all my heart". Halimo was always there for me whatever I wanted to do. She went with me and helped me forget all the bad things that had happened to me. We shared the root of our hearts. Can you ever forget such a beautiful friend?

One day we came back from the Madaras school together. We were a group of about 20 girls and boys. It was about 1:30pm in the afternoon. We separated because everybody had to walk in different directions to get home. Soon only Halimo and I were left. We decided to use a short-cut. It was a narrow path, bush-land with some trees. We were talking. Suddenly there were 3 grown-up men in front of us. They had guns. Four others showed up behind us. Halimo was the one who realized first that they were killers. She took my left hand, pulled me and we ran sideways into the bushes. One of them started shooting. It was rapid fire, one bullet hit my buttock, on the left side. At first I didn't feel the pain, then I noticed that my left leg was failing to function. It became awfully heavy. Then the pain came. It was a strong pumping kind of pain. I wanted to get away, so I grabbed my trousers with my hands and tried to pull the leg forward. I had worn white trousers that day. My left side was already full of blood. It was running down my leg, soaking the white cloth. My hands were full of blood, too. Then my leg became too weak. I fell down. Halimo was still pulling my hand. She tried to get me back up, so we could continue running. She was crying and shouting: "Get up, let's run, please! Abdul, let's run!" Her face was full of fear, her eyes were wide open, looking terrified. I couldn't talk; I was just looking at her. One of the men had already reached us and hit me with the back of his gun on the left side of my head from behind. I fainted. I must have been unconscious for about one minute. When I woke up I was lying on my stomach, bleeding. I felt the pain in my injured leg. I couldn't see properly. I touched and rubbed my eyes. I thought I would go blind. Everything I saw was red and flickering or flashing; like a red curtain in front of me. And then I saw Halimo, she was about 5 meters away, lying on her back. Two men were holding her arms. All 7 men were there. They were looking ugly; their cloths were dirty and torn. Halimo's clothes were torn and she was naked. One of the men had pulled down his trousers to his knees. I saw him penetrating her, moving up and down. One side of his face was very damaged. There was hardly any skin and the left eye was like pushed inside the scull. It was so ugly and disgusting, I was horrified. When I remember this, I start seeing everything red, like in that very moment. When I look at the faces of men in such a state of memory and fear, any face in front of me can turn into the face of that rapist. That's when I lose control. All I want is try to beat and chase the person. I can get very angry and aggressive. It sometimes happens even when it is the face of my father, or other people who I like and admire. Then I feel like as if there are two people inside me.

While the deformed man was raping Halimo, the others were standing there watching, laughing and constantly shooting into the air. These are the only sounds I could hear and they are ringing in my ear whenever I think of that day. Halimo's lips were swollen and bleeding. She was injured on her right cheek near the eye. Her eyes were open and dark. She seemed to be unconscious. I felt terrible pain. But I tried to move, shout, do anything, throw a stone at least, to make them stop, but I was frozen, paralyzed. I could not move. I was annoyed and very angry. My body failed me completely; I could not move at all. I was trapped. I felt so helpless and guilty. Since then I blame myself for not helping her, whereas she was always helping me so much. This guilt and sadness has weighed very heavy on me ever since. When the first man had finished the next one was raping her. He was the one with the scar. He pulled off his clothes in a hurry. He wore a long shirt. He was penetrating her, too. When I saw him moving up and down, I fainted again. It was just too much; it was too terrible to bear.

The next thing I remember was that I woke up seeing white things. There were voices talking. First I thought I was in another world, or dead, or something like that. I was in hospital. I saw blood dripping from a bottle on the right side of my bed. It was an infusion. My dad was there beside me. He was holding my hand. I was still fearing a lot. Then a doctor came and for the first time the face of an ordinary man turned into the disgusting face of the rapist. I was terrified and screamed: " This is the guy I saw and I know what he did!" I was furious and angry, full of tension. My dad tried to calm me down, but I shouted: "I will kill you!" My dad explained to me that it was just the doctor and that he wants to help me. My father also tried to find out what had happened to me, but I could not tell him.

After that incident I got a single room for a period of time. The nights in the hospital were horrible. I couldn't sleep. I saw the face of the rapist. I saw everything red when I remembered. I could not eat. I was blaming myself for what had happened. I was feeling guilty. I was terribly angry. A very deep feeling of darkness came into my heart and has never left me up to today. I had no future, no hope. After some time, when I seemed to have become more normal, it was decided that I should share a room again. But it didn't take long and I attacked my roommate. I shouted at him and pulled at his infusion because I thought he, too, was one of the rapists. So I was moved to a solitude room again. I was having nightmares about the rape scene and the dead bodies floating at the shore all the time. When I saw children playing and being happy I had to cry because I thought I could never do something like that again. I was in hospital for 3 months. In the end I was somehow okay again. Then the day I left the hospital, at the gate my dad and I met a stranger and again everything turned red and I saw the rapist in that innocent man. I ran after him, shouted at him, and wanted to hurt him. My father got me and held me tight. He said: "What is wrong with you? What's wrong?" I have never told him or anybody else what had happened to me exactly during that day of the rape and he also doesn't know what goes on in my mind and body when I get out of control. This is why I felt and still feel a certain distance to everybody around me. People don't understand why I act strange sometimes, and I cannot tell them.

Some time later Halimo's parents visited me at my home. They had brought gifts and wanted to see how I was doing. I could not face them. I could not open the door. I felt so bad and guilty. How could she ever forgive me for not having helped her when she needed me most? Sometimes she comes to me in my dreams, even now, and she looks beautiful and kind, just like she used to. But I cannot forgive myself. I don't even know whether she is still alive. I can't get myself to find out. I can't imagine how it would be to see her again. I only know I would run away.

After my days in the hospital my father took me to a friend of his. He lived in a small and quiet village. There were a lot of children in the village, playing football. I spend most of the time inside, just watching them, doing nothing. I was completely absent, far away, dealing with the darkness in my heart. After three weeks in the village I started to relax a bit. I ate more and slept a bit. Then fighting reached even this little remote village. One day at 12 o'clock noon, there was a heavy attack. There were explosions, fire, and the sounds of bullets all over the place. First, I was inside the house alone. People ran around and fled towards the forest. I was full of fear, shocked and paralyzed, but I ran behind the house. From there I could not move, I just stood there, my heart was racing and my whole body was shaking. Many people were passing by, some were injured, some shot, some were running although they were lacking an arm. One man lying very near to me on the ground was torn into two parts. A shell must have hit him. His upper part was lying far from his lower part, yet he was still crying and screaming. There was a lot of blood. The sight of him was horrible, it just looked so awful. All I did was close my eyes, I could not move. I don't know how long I was frozen there in terror and fear, crying until my dad came and carried me into a pickup. He was holding me as I was shaking and crying. I sat beside my dad and the driver in the front seat. Suddenly, as we were already heading out of the village, I bullet hit our driver through the front window. The glass shattered. The bullet went into the front of his head and something came out of his neck. The driver fell backwards and blood spilled over my eye. The vehicle lost control and we went into a ditch with great speed. When the pickup crashed I was catapulted out through the window and fainted. When I woke up I was lying halfway on the front of the car, halfway on the ground. I was more or less ok and immediately checked on my dad. He was unconscious, blood was coming out of his mouth and his shoulder and chest were injured. By that time people had come and they helped us on a truck to get to the nearby hospital. My father was unconscious for a long time. I kept sitting by his bedside, holding his hand and talking to him. I was scared he would not come back. I told him: "Don't worry. I'm ok. Please wake up, wake up!" I stayed in the hospital with my dad for two weeks, for there was no other place I could have gone to. Sometimes a guy came and gave me some fruits to eat.

When my dad was feeling better we went to friends and they brought us to G. There we met my aunt. We stayed there for a while. My dad had no job. He was just there with me thinking about what should happen to us in the future. I was feeling safer in G. but I had still problems with sleeping. After a while my aunty married and I was somehow happy, but there was nothing I could enjoy any more, even the marriage party was not enjoyable for me.

Then we decided to move on to U. In U. I made new friends and one day we met at a friend's place to watch the movie "Black Hawk Down." It is a film about the war in Somalia. At first it was okay, but when the shooting in the film started and a lot of blood was shown I got out of control. I started to see everything red, I was breathing fast, my heart was racing. I got scared, furious, angry. I started shaking and then I took a chair and threw it into the TV screen. The television exploded and everybody screamed and shouted. I didn't realize the panic and chaos around me. It was like I was not in my world anymore. I was full of panic, I ran out of the room and down the stairs. I fell and cut my tongue badly, blood was dripping out of my mouth and on my trousers. I was still in total shock and panic when they found me. I was taken to hospital and treated for about one month. I could not talk properly for some time because my tongue was swollen and stitched together. My dad did not understand what had happened. He just said he had to pay a lot of money for the damage that I had done.

In those days we were living with another aunt, actually it was not my aunt, it was the wife of one of my dad's friends. Altogether we spent about one year in U. My dad was unemployed during that time, but he was helping the friends we stayed with.

Then in 1999 my dad got to know a woman from Tanzania in U. They decided to get married and we moved to the refugee camp in 2000. The woman is okay, although I don't talk to her too much. She also doesn't know anything about my past and I don't know what she thinks is wrong with me when I get out of control. Sometimes she makes an effort and tries to talk to me. She asks me questions about my experiences in the past, but I cannot tell her. She tries, but still I do not feel very close to her.

Even now, many years later, the pictures of the day when Halimo got raped keep coming back to my mind. I look at normal people, like a teacher or a friend, and suddenly the face of the rapist appears. Then I get angry and aggressive and try to hurt the person. I throw things and get violent. Sometimes I find myself sitting in strange places, like on top of the roof, crying, and I have no idea how I got there. It is as if there are two personalities living inside me. One is smart and kind and normal, the other one is crazy and violent. I try so hard to control this other side of me. But I fail. Sometimes I feel tears running down my cheek and I wonder why. Sometimes I walk down the street and suddenly I see the path in the bush of that day in front of me and I feel Halimo's hand pulling my hand, trying to make me run and escape together. Since that day I can't walk shortcuts anymore. Even a normal bush can bring back all these memories. And when the memory of the rape comes, all the other pictures are in my mind as well, like the dead bodies in the ocean. Since we are in the camp it is especially bad, since there is so much bush land around.

Now that I have talked about all that has happened to me, I would also like my father to know. I want him to read my story. I also want to register now with the Red Cross Tracing Service, to find Halimo. Maybe she is still in

Somalia or lives as a refugee in Nairobi. Wherever she is now, I want to find out how her life is today. May be she will write to me or we can even meet? Until today, I have never started a friendship with a girl again. I didn't want to get close to them anymore. They remind me of what happened to Halimo and me. In the future I wish I can live like a normal person, get married, and have children. I would like to be a doctor or a lawyer. I would love to help people.

Date and Place:

_____          _____          _____

Signature Survivor                          Signature Therapist                          Signature Interpreter

# Appendix C: Who is vivo

*Who is vivo*

vivo is an alliance of professionals experienced in research and service provision in the fields of psychotraumatology, public health, human rights advocacy, humanitarian aid, behavioral neuroscience and sustainable development.

*vivo's mission*

vivo works to overcome and prevent traumatic stress and its consequences within the individual as well as the community, safeguarding the rights and dignity of people affected by violence and conflict. vivo further aims to strengthen local resources for the development of peaceful, human rights-based, societal ways of living.

*vivo's program areas*

vivo focuses on traumatic stress in different societal and cultural settings. Scientific research is carried out in the field to systematically learn from the victims themselves and disseminate their knowledge. The organization develops, implements, and evaluates evidence-based best practice interventions. vivo provides training for local and international professionals who assist those who have fallen victim to psychological trauma and human rights abuse. The organization raises awareness among the general public and decision makers on issues related to trauma and its consequences. vivo documents violations of human rights and helps those affected find redress by working with national and international agencies. Scientists, field practitioners, and those affected are brought together by the organization to foster collaboration and partnership building for multi-disciplinary trauma and mental health program development.

*Contact address of vivo and the authors:*

Dr. Maggie Schauer, Ass.-Prof. Dr. Frank Neuner, Prof. Dr. Thomas Elbert, are all at the vivo Outpatient Clinic and at the University of Konstanz

Postal address:

Centre for Psychiatry, Feursteinstr. 55 Haus 22, D-78479 Reichenau, Germany; phone: +49-7531-88-4623 fax: +49-7531-88-4601

email: info@vivo.org
url: www.vivo.org

# References

Agger, I. (1994). *Trauma and testimony among refugee women: A psycho-social exploration.* London: Zed Books.

Agger, I. , & Jensen, S. B. (1990). Testimony as ritual and evidence in psychotherapy for political prisoners. *Journal of Traumatic Stress, 3,* 115–130.

AMANI. (1997). *A trauma counselling handbook.* Harare, Zimbabwe: Amani Trust.

American Psychiatric Association. (1994). *Diagnostic and Statistical Manual* (4th ed.). New York: APA.

American Psychiatric Association. (1997). *Let's talk facts about mental illnesses – An overview*; Retrieved from www.psych.org/public_info/

Amnesty International. (2003). *Definitions of torture.* Retrieved January 7, 2003, from http://www.amnesty.org.uk/torture/definition.shtml

Baddely, A. L. (1990). *Human memory.* Boston: Allyn & Bacon.

Basoglu, M., Paker, M., Ozmen, E., Tasdemir, O., & Sahin, D. (1994). Factors related to long-term traumatic stress responses in survivors of torture in Turkey. *JAMA, 272,* 357–363.

Bauer, P. J. (1996). What do infants recall of their lives? Memory for specific events by one- to two-years-olds. *American Psychologist, 51,* 29–41.

Bettelheim, B. (1986). *Surviving the Holocaust.* Fontana: Flamingo.

Bisbey, S., & Bisbey, L. B. (1998) *Brief therapy for post-traumatic stress disorder: Traumatic incident reduction and related techniques.* Chichester, UK: John Wiley & Sons.

Bock, J., Helmeke, C., Ovtscharoff, W., Gruß, M., & Braun, K. (2003). Frühkindliche emotionale Erfahrungen beeinflussen die funktionelle Entwicklung des Gehirns. *NeuroForum, 2,* 51–57.

Bonne, O., Brandes, D., Gilboa, A., Gomori, J. M., Shenton, M. E., Pitman, R. K., & Shalev, A. Y. (2001). Longitudinal MRI study of hippocampal volume in trauma survivors with PTSD. *American Journal of Psychiatry, 158,* 8.

Bremner, J. D., Randall, P., Vermetten, E., Staib, L., Bronen, R. A., Mazure, Capelli S., McCarthy G., Innis, R. B., & Charney, D. S. (1997) Magnetic resonance imaging-based measurement of hippocampal volume in posttraumatic stress disorder related to childhood physical and sexual abuse – A preliminary report. *Biological Psychiatry, 41,* 23–32.

Bremner, J. D. (1999). Alterations in brain structure and function associated with posttraumatic stress disorder. *Seminars in Clinical Neuropsychiatry, 4,* 249–255.

Bremner, J. D. (2002), *Does stress damage the brain? Understanding traumarelated disorders from a mind-body perspective.* New York: W. W. Norton.

Bremner, J. D., Krystal, J. H., Southwick, S. M., & Charney, D. S. (1995). Functional neuroanatomical correlates of the effects of stress on memory. *Journal of Traumatic Stress, 8,* 527–545.

Bremner, J. D., Vythilingam, M., Vermetten, E., Southwick, S. M., McGlashan, T., Nazeer, A., Khan, S., Vaccarino, L. V., Soufer, R., Garg, P. K., Ng, C. K., Staib, L. H., Duncan., J. S. & Charney, D. S. (2003). MRI and PET study of deficits in hippocampal structure and function in women with childhood sexual abuse and posttraumatic stress disorder. *American Journal of Psychiatry 160,* 924–932.

Breslau, N. (2001). Outcomes of posttraumatic stress disorder. *Journal of Clinical Psychiatry, 62* (Suppl. 17), 55–59.

Brewin, C. R. (2001). A cognitive neuroscience account of posttraumatic stress disorder and its treatment. *Behaviour Research and Therapy, 39,* 373–393.

Brewin, C. R., Andrews, B., & Valentine, J. D. (2000). Meta-analysis of risk factors for posttraumatic stress disorder in trauma-exposed adults. *Journal of Consulting and Clinical Psychology, 68,* 748–766.

Brewin, C. R., Dalgleish, T., & Joseph, S. (1996). A dual representation theory of posttraumatic stress disorder. *Psychological Review, 103,* 670–686.

Brewin, C. R., Watson, M., McCarthy, S., Hyman, P., & Dayson, D. (1998). Intrusive memories and depression in cancer patients. *Behaviour Research Therapy, 36,* 1131–1142.

Buchanan, T.W. & Lovallo, W.R. (2001). Enhanced memory for emotional material following stress-level cortisol treatment in humans. *Psychoneuroendocrinology, 26,* 307–317.

Byrne, C. A., & Riggs, D. S. (1996). The cycle of trauma; relationship aggression in male Vietnam veterans with symptoms of posttraumatic stress disorder. *Violence Vict, 11,* 213–225.

Cahill, L., Prins, B., Weber, M., & McGaugh, J. L. (1994). Beta-adrenergic activation and memory for emo-tional events. *Nature, 371,* 702–704.

Cahill, L., Babinsky, R., Markowitsch, H. J., & McGaugh, J. L. (1995). The amygdala and emotional memory. *Nature, 377,* 295–296.

Castles, S., & Miller, M. J. (1993). *The age of migration: International population movements in the modern world.* New York: The Guilford Press.

Cienfuegos, J., & Monelli, C. (1983). The testimony of political repression as a therapeutic instrument. *American Journal of Orthopsychiatry, 53,* 43–51.

Conway, M. A. (2001). Sensory-perceptual episodic memory and its context: autobiographical memory. *Philosophical Transactions of the Royal Society of London Series B: Biological Science, 356,* 1375–1384.

Conway, M. A., & Pleydell-Pearce, C. W. (2000). The construction of autobiographical memories in the self-memory system. *Psychological Review, 107,* 261–288.

Cunningham, M., & Cunningham, J. D. (1997). Patterns of symptomatology and patterns of torture and trauma experiences in resettled refugees. *Australian and New Zealand Journal of Psychiatry, 31,* 555–565.

Deblinger, E., Steer, R. A., & Lippmann, J. (1999). Two-year follow-up study of cognitive and behavioural therapy for sexually abused children suffering post-traumatic stress symptoms. *Child Abuse & Neglect, 23,* 1271–1378.

de Quervain, D. J. -F., Roozendaal, B., & McGaugh, J. L. (1998). Stress and glucocorticoids impair retrieval of long-term spatial memory. *Nature, 394,* 787–790.

de Quervain, D. J. -F., Roozendaal, B., Nitsch, R. M., McGaugh, J. L., & Hock, C. (2000). Acute cortisone ad-ministration impairs retrieval of long-term declarative memory in humans. *Nature Neurosci., 3*, 313–314.

de Quervain, D. J. -F., Henke, K. Aerni, A., Treyer, V., McGaugh, J. L., Berthold, T., Nitsch, R. M., Buck F., Roozendaal, B., & Hock, C. (2003). Glucocorticoid-induced impairment of declarative memory retrieval is associated with reduced blood flow in the medial temporal lobe. *European Journal of Neuroscience, 17*, 1296–1302.

Derriennic, J. P. (1971). Theory and ideologies of violence. *Journal of Peace Research, 8*, 361–374.

Dyregrov, A., Gupta, L., Gjestad, R., & Mukanoheli, E. (2000). Trauma exposure and psychological reactions to genocide among Rwandan children. *Journal of Traumatic Stress, 13*, 3–21.

Ehlers, A., & Clark, D. M. (2000). A cognitive model of posttraumatic stress disorder. *Behaviour Research and Therapy, 38*, 319–345.

Elbert, T., & Schauer, M. (2002) Burnt into memory, *Nature, 412*, 883.

Elbert, T., & Rockstroh, B. (2003). Stress factors. The science of our flexible responses to an unpredictable world. *Nature, 421*, 477–478.

Elbert, T., Schauer, M., Neuner, F., Wienbruch, C., Borgelt, J., & Rockstroh, B. (2003, May). *Identification of dysfunctional brain areas in survivors of severe organized violence.* Paper presented at the ESTSS Conference (European Society for Traumatic Stress Studies), Berlin, Germany

Elbert, T., Huschka, B., Schauer, E., Schauer, M., Somasundaram, D., Hirth, M., & Neuner, F. (in press) Trauma-related impairment in children – An epidemiological survey in Sri Lankan provinces affected by two decades of civil war and unrest.

Foa, E. B. (1995). *Post-traumatic Stress Diagnostic Scale (PDS).* Minneapolis: National Computer Systems.

Foa, E. B. (2000). Psychosocial treatment of posttraumatic stress disorder. *Journal of Clinical Psychiatry, 61(Suppl. 5)*, 43–48; discussion 49–51.

Foa, E. B., & Kozak, M. J. (1986). Emotional processing of fear: Exposure to corrective information. *Psychological Bulletin, 99*, 20–35.

Foa, E. B., & Meadows, E. A. (1997). Psychosocial treatments for posttraumatic stress disorder. *Annual Review of Psychology, 48*, 449–480.

Foa, E. B., & Rothbaum, B. O. (1998). *Treating the trauma of rape: Cognitive-behavioral therapy for PTSD.* New York: The Guilford Press.

Foa, E. B., Dancu, C. V., Hembree, E. A., Jaycox, L. H., Meadows, E. A., & Street, G. P. (1999). A comparison of exposure therapy, stress inoculation training, and their combination for reducing posttraumatic stress disorder in female assault victims. *Journal of Consulting and Clinical Psychology, 67*, 194–200.

Foa, E. B., Davidson, J. R. T.; & Frances, A. (1999). The expert consensus guideline series. Treatment of Posttraumatic Stress disorder. *Journal of Clinical Psychiatry, 60*, 4–76.

Foa, E. B., Hearst-Ikeda, D., & Perry, K. J. (1995). Evaluation of a brief cognitive-behavioral program for the prevention of chronic PTSD in recent assault victims. *Journal of Consulting and Clinical Psychology, 63*, 948–955.

Foa, E. B., Molnar, C., & Cashman, L. (1995). Change in rape narratives during exposure therapy for posttraumatic stress disorder. *Journal of Traumatic Stress, 4*, 675–690.

Foa, E. B., Riggs, D. S., & Gershuny, B. S. (1995). Arousal, numbing, and intrusion: symptom structure of PTSD following assault. *American Journal of Psychiatry, 152*, 116–120.

Foa, E. B., Rothbaum, B. O., Riggs, D. S., & Murdock, T. B. (1991). Treatment of posttraumatic stress disorder in rape victims: A comparison between cognitive-behavioral procedures and counseling. *Journal of Consulting and Clinical Psychology, 59*, 715–723.

Forbes Martin, S. (1991). *Refugee women.* London & New Jersey: Zed Books.

Frankl, V. (1946). *Ein Psycholog erlebt das Konzentrationslager* [A psychologist's experience of a concentration camp]. Vienna: Verlag für Jugend und Volk.

Friedman, M. J., & Jaranson, J. M. (2002). The applicability of the PTSD concept to refugees. In A. J. Marsella, T. H. Borneman, S. Ekblad, & J. Orley (Eds.), *Amidst peril and pain: The mental health and well-being of the world's refugees.* Washington, DC: American Psychological Association.

Friedman, M. J. (2000). *Posttraumatic stress disorder – The latest assessment and treatment strategies.* Compact Clinicals. New York: APA.

Galtung, J. (1969). Violence, peace, and peace research. *Journal of Peace Research, 6*, 167–191.

Garcia-Peltoniemi, R. E. (1991). Clinical manifestations of psychopathology. In *Mental health services for refugees.* Rockville, MD: US Department of Health and Human Services, National Institute of Mental Health.

Goenjian, A. K., Karayan, I., Pynoos, R. S., Minassian, D., Najarian, L. M., Steinberg, A. M., & Fairbanks, L. A. (1997). Outcome of psychotherapy among early adolescents after trauma. *American Journal of Psychiatry, 154*, 536–542.

Harrell-Bond, B. E. (1986). *Imposing aid: Emergency assistance to refugees.* Oxford: Oxford University Press.

Harvey, A. G., & Bryant, R. A. (1999). A qualitative investigation of the organization of traumatic memories. *British Journal of Clinical Psychology, 38*, 401–405.

Herman, J. L. (1992). *Trauma and recovery.* New York: Basic Books.

Herman, J. L. (1992). Complex PTSD: A syndrome in survivors of prolonged and repeated trauma. *Journal of Traumatic Stress, 5*, 377–391.

Howe, M. L., Courage, M. L., & Peterson, C. (1994) How can I remember when "I" wasn't there: Long-term retention of traumatic experiences and emerge of the cognitive self. *Consciousness and Cognition, 3*, 327–355.

Jaycox, L. H., Foa, E. B., & Morral, A. R. (1998). Influence of emotional engagement and habituation on exposure therapy for PTSD. *Journal of Consulting and Clinical Psychology, 66*, 185–192.

Jones, D. P. H., & Krugman, R. D. (1986). Can a three-year-old child bear witness to her sexual assault and attempted murder? *Child Abuse & Neglect, 10*, 253–258.

Karunakara, U., Neuner, F., Schauer, M., Singh, K., Hill, K., Elbert, T., & Burnham, G. (2004). Traumatic events and symptoms of post-traumatic stress disorder amongst Sudanese nationals, refugees and Ugandan nationals in the West Nile. *African Health Sciences, 4,* 83–93.

Kearney, C. (1999). *World Mission Day: Surviving a Refugee School in Uganda.* Retrieved November 21, 2001, from http://www.catholicweekly.com.au/99/oct/76.html

Kessler, R. C., Sonnega, A., Bromet, E., Hughes, M., & Nelson, C. B. (1995). Posttraumatic stress disorder in the National Comorbidity Survey. *Archives of General Psychiatry, 52,* 1048–1060.

Kim, J. J., & Yoon, K. S. (1998). Stress: Metaplastic effects in the hippocampus. *Trends in Neuroscience, 21,* 505–509.

Kinzie, J. D., Sack, W. H., Angell R. H., & Clarke, G. (1989). A three-year follow-up of Cambodian young people traumatized as children. *Journal of the American Academy of Child and Adolescent Psychiatry, 28,* 501–504.

Koss, M. P., Tromp, S., & Tharan, M. (1995) Traumatic Memories: Empirical foundation, clinical and forensic implications. *Clinical Psychology: Research and Practice, 2,* 111–132.

Lang, P. J. (1977). Imagery in therapy: An information processing analysis of fear. *Behavior Therapy, 8,* 862–866.

Lang, P. J. (1979). A bio-informational theory of emotional imagery. *Psychophysiology, 16,* 195–512.

Lang, P. J. (1984). Dead Souls: Or why the neurobehavioral science of emotion should pay attention to cognitive science. In Th. Elbert, B. Rockstroh, W. Lutzenberger, & N. Birbaumer (Eds.), *Self-regulation of the brain and behaviour* (pp. 255–272). Berlin: Springer Verlag.

Lang, P. J. (1993). The network model of emotion: Motivational connections. In R. Wyer & T. Scrull (Eds.), *Advances in social cognition, VI.* Hillsdale, NJ: Lawrence Erlbaum Associate.

LeDoux, J. E. (2000). Emotion Circuits in the brain. *Annual Review of Neuroscience, 23,* 155–184.

LeDoux, J. E. (1995). Emotion: Clues from the brain. *Annual Review of Psychology, 46,* 209–235.

Macksound, M. S., Dyregrov, A., & Raundalen, M. (1993). Traumatic war experiences and their effects on children. In J. P. Wilson & B. Raphael (Eds.), *International handbook of traumatic stress syndromes* (pp. 625-634). New York: Plenum Press.

Malkki, L. H. (1995). *Purity and exile: Violence memory, and national cosmology among Hutu refugees in Tanzania.* Chicago: The University of Chicago Press.

McCann, I. L., Sakheim, D. K., & Anbrahamson, D. J. (1988). Trauma and victimization: A model of psychological adaptation. *Counseling Psychologist, 16,* 531–594.

McClelland, J. L., McNaughton, B. L., & O'Reilly, R. C. (1995). Why there are complementary learning systems in the hippocampus and neocortex: Insights from the successes and failures of connectionist models of learning and memory. *Psychological Review, 102,* 419–457.

McGaugh, J. L. (2002). Memory consolidation and the amygdala: A systems perspective. *Trends in Neuro-science, 25,* 456.

McEwen, B. S. (1999). Stress and hippocampal plasticity. *Annual Review of Neuroscience, 22,* 105–122.

McEwen, B. S. (2002). The end of stress as we know it. Washington DC: Joseph Henry Press/Dana Press.

McFarlane, A. C., Atchison, M., Rafalowicz, E., & Papay, P. (1994). Physical symptoms in post-traumatic stress disorder. *Journal of Psychosomatic Research, 38,* 715–726.

Meaney, M., Aitken, D., van Berkel, C., Bhatnagar, C., & Sapolsky, R. (1988). Effects of neonatal handling on age-related impairments associated with the hippocampus. *Science, 239,* 766–770.

Metcalfe, J., & Jacobs, W. (1996). A hot-system/cool-system view of memory under stress. *PTSD Research Quarterly, 7,* 1–3.

Misch, P., Phillips, M., Evans, P., & Berelowitz, M. (1993). Trauma in pre-school children: A clinical account. In G. Forrest, *Trauma and crisis management.* London: ACPP Publications.

Nader, K., Schafe, G. E., & LeDoux, J. E. (2000). Fear memories require protein synthesis in the amygdala for consolidation after retrieval. *Nature, 406,* 722.

Neuner, F., Schauer, M., Elbert, T., & Roth, W. T. (2002). A narrative exposure treatment as intervention in a Macedonia's refugee camp: a case report. *Journal of Behavioural and Cognitive Psychotherapy, 30,* 205–209.

Neuner, F., Schauer, M., Klaschik, C., Karunakara, U., & Elbert, T. (2004a). A comparison of narrative exposure therapy, supportive counseling and psychoeducation for treating posttraumatic stress disorder in an African refugee settlement. *Journal of Consulting and Clinical Psychology, 72,* 579–587.

Neuner, F., Schauer, M., Karunakara, U., Klaschik, C., Robert C., & Elbert, T. (2004b) Psychological trauma and evidence for enhanced vulnerability for PTSD through previous trauma in West Nile refugees. *BMC Psychiatry, 4,* 34.

Nutt, D. J., & Malizia, A. L. (2004). Structural and functional brain changes in posttraumatic stress disorder. *Journal of Clinical Psychiatry, 65,* (suppl. 1), 11–17.

Onyut, L. P., Neuner, F., Schauer, E., Ertl, V., Odenwald, M., Schauer, M., & Elbert, T. (2004a). The Nakivale Camp Mental Health Project: Building local competency for psychological assistance to traumatised refugees. *Intervention, 2*(2), 90–107.

Onyut, P. L., Neuner, F., Schauer, E., Ertl, V., Hoogeven, M., Odenwald, M., Schauer, M., & Elbert, T. (in press). Narrative exposure therapy as a treatment for child war and conflict survivors with posttraumatic stress disorder: An uncontrolled clinical trial.

Onyut, P. L, Neuner F, Schauer E, Ertl V, Odenwald, M., Elbert T (2004b). *Prevalence of Post Traumatic Stress Disorder among Somali and Rwandese Refugees living in The Nakivale Camp.* Submitted for publication.

Ozer, E. J., Best, S. R., Lipsey, T. L., & Weiss, D. S. (2003). Predictors of posttraumatic stress disorder and symptoms in adults: A meta-analysis. *Psychological Bulletin, 129,* 52–73.

Papageorgiou, V., Frangou-Garunovic, A., Iordanidou, R., Yule, W., Smith, P., & Vostanis P. (2000). War trauma and psychopathology in Bosnian refugee children. *European Child and Adolescent Psychiatry, 9,* 84–90.

Pelcovitz, D., van der Kolk, B., Roth, S., Mandel, F., Kaplan, S., & Resick, P. (1997). Development of a criteria set and a structured interview for disorders of extreme stress (SIDES). *Journal of Traumatic Stress, 10,* 3–16.

Peterson, C. (1996). The preschool child witness: Errors in account of traumatic injury. *Canadian Journal of Behavioural Science, 28,* 36–42.

Pine, D. S., & Cohen, J. A. (2002). Trauma in children and adolescents: risk and treatment of psychiatric sequelae. *Biological Psychiatry, 51,* 519–531.

Raundalen, M., Lwanga, J., Mugisha, C., & Dyregrov, A. (1987). Four investigations on stress among children in Uganda. In C. P. Dodge & M. Raundalen (Eds.), *War, violence and children in Uganda* (pp. 83-108). Oslo: Norwegian University Press

Reviere, S. L. (1996). *Memory of childhood trauma: A clinician's guide to the literature.* New York: Guilford Press.

Riggs, D. S., Byrne, C. A., Weathers, F. W., & Litz, B. T. (1998). The quality of the intimate relationships of male Vietnam veterans: Problems associated with posttraumatic stress disorder. *Journal of Traumatic Stress, 11,* 87–101.

Robinson, J. A. (1992). First experience memories: Contexts and function in personal histories. In M. A. Conway, D. C. Rubin, H. Spinnler, & W. A. Wagenaar (Eds.), *Theoretical perspectives on autobiographical memories* (pp. 223–239). Dodrecht, The Netherlands: Kluwer Academics.

Rockstroh, B., Ray, W., Wienbruch, C., & Elbert, T. (in press). Identification of dysfunctional cortical network architecture and communication: Abnormal slow wave activity mapping (ASWAM) in neurological and psychiatric disorders. *BMC Neuroscience.*

Roozendaal, B., Griffith, Q. K., Buranday, J., de Quervain, D. J. -F., & McGaugh, J. L. (2003). The hippocampus mediates glucocorticoid-induced retrieval impairments of spatial memory: Dependence on the basolateral amygdala. *Proceedings of the National Academy of Science of the U S A, 100,* 1328–1333.

Roozendaal, B., de Quervain, D. J. -F., Ferry, B., Setlow, B., McGaugh,J .L. (2001). Basolateral amygdala-nucleus accumbens interactions in mediating glucocorticoid enhancement of memory consolidation. *Journal of Neuroscience, 21,* 2518–2525.

Rosenthal, G. (1997). Traumatische Familienvergangenheiten [Traumatic family backgrounds]. In G. Rosenthal (Ed.), *Der Holocaust im Leben von drei Generationen [The Holocaust in the lives of three generations].* Gießen, Germany: Psychosozial-Verlag.

Rothbaum B. O., Foa, E. B., Rigge, D. S., Murdoch, T., & Walsh, W. A. (1992). Prospective examination of post-traumatic stress disorder in rape victims. *Journal of Traumatic Stress, 5,* 455–475.

Rothbaum, B. O., & Foa, B. F. (1999). Exposure therapy for PTSD. *PTSD Research Quarterly, 10*(2), 1–3.

Rudy, J. W., & Sutherland, R. J. (1994). The memory coherence problem, configural associations, and the hippocampal system. In D. L. Schachter & E. Tulving (Eds). *Memory systems* (pp. 119–146). Cambridge: MIT Press.

Saigh, P. A. (1991). The development of post-traumatic stress disorder following four different types of traumatizations. *Behaviour Research & Therapy, 29,* 213–216.

Saigh, P. A. (1992). The behavioural treatment of child and adolescent post-traumatic stress disorder. *Advances in Behaviour Research & Therapy, 14,* 247–275.

Saigh, P. A., Yule, W., & Inamdar, S. C. (1996). Imaginal flooding of traumatized children and adolescents. *Journal of School Psychology, 34,* 163–183 .

Saltzman, W. R., Layne, C. M., Steinberg, A. M., Arslanagic, B., & Pynoos, R. S. (2003). Developing a culturally and ecologically sound intervention program for youth exposed to war and terrorism. *Child and Adolescent Psychiatric Clinics of Northern America, 12,* 319–342.

Schachter, D. L. (1987). Implicit memory: History and current status. *Journal of Experimental Psychology: Learning, Memory and Cognition, 13,* 501–518.

Schacter, D. L. (1996). Searching for memory: The brain, the mind and the past. New York: Basic Books.

Sapolsky, R. M. (1999). Glucocorticoids, stress, and their adverse neurological effects: Relevance to aging. *Experimental Gerontology, 34*(6), 721-732.

Schauer, E., Neuner, F., Elbert, T., Ertl, V., Onyut, L., Odenwald, M., & Schauer, M. (2004). Narrative exposure therapy in children – A case study. *Intervention, 2*(1), 18–32.

Schauer, M., Karunakara, U., Neuner, F., Klaschik, C., Kley, E., Rockstroh, B., et al. (2001, May). *High prevalence of PTSD in African victims of organized violence: A demographic survey in the West-Nile region of Uganda and Sudan.* Paper presented at the 7th European Conference on Traumatic Stress Studies, Edinburgh, United Kingdom.

Schauer, M., Neuner, F., Karunakara, U. K., Klaschik, C., & Elbert T. (2002). PTSD and the building block effect of psychological trauma among West-Nile Africans. *ESTSS Bulletin, 4.*

Schnurr, P. P., & Jankowski, M. K. (2002). Physical health and posttraumtic stress disorder: Review and synthesis. *Seminars in Clinical Neuropsychiatry, 4*(4), 295–304.

Segerstrom, S. C., & Miller, G. E. (2004). Psychological stress and the human immune system: A meta-analytic study of 30 years of inquiry. *Psychological Bulletin, 130,* 601–630.

Shalev, A. Y., Sahar, T., Freedman, S., Peri, T., Glick, N., Brandes, D., Orr, S., & Pitman, R. K. (1998). A prospective study of heart rate responses following trauma and the subsequent development of PTSD. *Archives of General Psychiatry, 55,* 553–559.

Shalev, A. Y., Peri, T., Canetti, L. et al. (1996). Predictors of PTSD in injured trauma survivors: A prospective study. *American Journal of Psychiatry, 143,* 219–225.

Shastri, L. (2002). Episodic memory and cortico-hippocampal interactions. *Trends in Cognitive Sciences, 6,* 162–168.

Shrestha, N. M., Sharma, B., Van Ommeren, M., Regmi, S., Makaju, R., Komproe, I., Shrestha, G. B. & de Jong, J. T. V. M. (1998). Impact of torture on refugees displaced within the developing world: symptomatology among Bhutanese refugees in Nepal. *JAMA, 280,* 443–448.

Shum, M. S. (1998). The role of temporal landmarks in autobiographical memory processes. *Psychological Bulletin, 124,* 423–442.

Somasundaram, D. J., & Sivayokan, S. (1994). War trauma in a civilian population. *British Journal of Psychiatry, 165,* 524–527.

Somasundaram, D. J. (1993). *Child trauma.* Jaffna: University of Jaffna, Sri Lanka

Somasundaram, D. J. (2002). Child soldiers: Understanding the context. *British Medical Journal, 324,* 1268–1271.

Southwick, S. M., Krystal, J. H., Morgan, C. A., Johnson, D., Nagy, L. M., Nicolaou, A., Heninger G. R., Charney D. S. (1993). Abnormal noradrenergic function in posttraumatic stress disorder. *Archives of General Psychiatry, 50,* 266–274.

Staub, E. (1998). Breaking the cycle of genocidal violence: Healing and reconciliation, In J. H. Harvey (Ed), *Perspectives on loss: A sourcebook. Death, dying, and bereavement.* Philadelphia, PA: Brunner/Mazel, Inc.

Streans, S. D. (1992). *Psychological distress and relief work: who helps the helpers?* Oxford: Refugees Studies Programme, University of Oxford.

Steil, R., & Straube E.R. (2002). Posttraumatische Belastungsstörungen bei Kindern und Jugendlichen [Posttraumatic stress disorders in children and adolescents]. *Zeitschrift für Klinische Psychologie und Psychotherapie, 31,* 1–13.

Steil, R. (2000). Post-traumatische Belastungsstörung [Posttraumatic stress disorder]. In M. Hatzinger (Ed.) *Kognitive Verhaltenstherapie psychischer Störungen* [Cognitive behavior therapy of psychological disorders]. Weinheim: PVU

Steil, R., & Ehlers, A. (1996). Die posttraumatische Belastungsstörung: Eine Übersicht [Posttraumatic stress disorder: An overview]. *Verhaltensmodifikation und Verhaltensmedizin, 17,* 169–212.

Stein, A. (1993). *Hidden children.* London: Viking.

Stein, B. D., Jaycox, L. H., Kataoka, S. H., Wong, M., Tu, W., Elliott, M. N., et al. (2003). A mental health intervention for schoolchildren exposed to violence: A randomized controlled trial. *JAMA, 290,* 603–611.

Sullivan, M. A., Saylor, C. F., & Foster, K. Y. (1991). Post-hurricane adjustment of preschoolers and their families. *Advances in Behaviour Research and Therapy, 13,* 163–171.

Tandon, Y. (1984). Ugandan refugees in Kenya: A community of enforced self-reliance. *Disasters, 8,* 267–271.

Tauber, C. D. (2003). *Psychological trauma, physical health and conflict resolution in Croatia, Serbia and Bosnia: Lessons for the future.* Retrieved on 17.02.2003 from www.conflictres.org/vol184/tauber.htm

Teicher, M. H., Andersen, S. L., Polcari, A., Anderson, C. M., & Navalta, C. P. (2002). Developmental neurobiology of childhood stress and trauma. *Psychiatric Clinics of North America, 25,* 397–426.

Terr, L. (1993). *Unchained memories.* New York: Basic Books.

Terr, L. C. (1988). What happens to early memories of trauma? A study of twenty children under age five at the time of documented traumatic events. *Journal of the American Academy of Child and Adolescent Psychiatry, 27,* 96–104.

Tessler, M., & Nelson, K. (1994). Making memories: The influence of joint encoding on later recall by young children. *Consciousness and Cognition, 3,* 307–326.

Thabet, A. A., & Vostanis, P. (1999). Post-traumatic stress reactions in children of war. *The Journal of Child Psychology and Psychiatry, 40,* 385–391.

Thabet, A. A., & Vostanis, P. (2000). Post traumatic stress disorder reactions in children of war: A longitudinal study. *Child Abuse and Neglect, 24,* 291–298.

Tulving, E. (2001). Episodic memory and common sense: how far apart? *Philosophical Transactions of the Royal Society of London Series B: Biological Science, 356,* 1505–1515.

Tulving, E., & Markowitsch, H. J. (1998). Episodic and declarative memory: role of the hippocampus. *Hippocampus, 8,* 198–204.

Turner, S. (1999). *Angry young men in camps: Gender, age and class relations among Burundian refugees in Tanzania* (Working Paper No. 9). Roskilde: Roskilde University, Institute of Development Studies.

United Nations. (1984). *Convention against torture and other cruel, inhuman or degrading treatment or punishment.* Retrieved on January, 7, 2003, from http://www.unhchr.ch/html/menu3/b/h_cat39.htm

UNHCR. (2002a). *Extensive abuse of West African refugee children reported.* Retrieved on June 9, 2002, from http://www.unhcr.ch/

UNHCR. (2002b). *Statistical yearbook 2001.* Geneva: UNHCR.

UNICEF. (2001). *The state of the world's children 2001.* New York: UNICEF.

USCR. (2001). *Uganda: 2000 Country Report.* Retrieved on July 10, 2001, from http://www.refugees.org

van der Gaag, N. (1996). Field of dreams: Life in a refugee settlement. *New Internationalist.*

van der Kolk, B. (1995). Dissociation and the fragmentary nature of traumatic memories: overview and exploratory study. *Journal of Traumatic Stress, 8,* 4.

van der Kolk, B. A. (1994). The body keeps the score: Memory and the evolving psychobiology of posttraumatic stress. *Harvard Review of Psychiatry, 1,* 253–265.

van der Kolk, B. A. (1996). Trauma and memory. In B. A. van der Kolk, A. C. McFarlane, & L. Weisaeth (Eds.), *Traumatic stress.* New York: Guilford Press.

van der Kolk, B. A. (1997). The psychobiology of posttraumatic stress disorder. *Journal of Clinical Psychiatry, 58*(Suppl 9), 16–24.

van der Kolk, B. A., Roth, S., Pelcovitz, D., & Mandel, F. (1993). *Complex PTSD: Results of the PTSD field trials for DSM-IV.* Washington, DC: American Psychiatric Association.

van der Veer, G. (1998). *Counseling and therapy with refugees and victims of trauma* (Vol. 2). West Sussex: Wiley.

van Emmerik, A. A., Kamphuis, J. H., Hulsbosch, A. M., & Emmelkamp, P. M. (2002). Single session debriefing after psychological trauma: a meta-analysis. *The Lancet, 360,* 766–771.

van Velsen, C., Gorst-Unsworth, C., & Turner, S. (1996). Survivors of torture and organized violence: demography and diagnosis. *Journal of Traumatic Stress, 9,* 181–193.

Veronen, L. J., & Kilpatrick, D. G. (1983). Stress management for rape victims. In D. Meichenbaum & M. E. Jaremko (Eds.), *Stress reduction and prevention* (pp. 341–479). New York: Plenum Press.

vivo (2003) Epidemiological Survey of Children's Mental Health in the Vanni Region, Ministry of Human Resources Development, Education and Cultural Affairs & GTZ/BECARE: Kilinochichi and Colombo, Sri Lanka.

vivo (2002). BESP/BECARE mid-term review for GTZ. Konstanz, Germany.

vivo. *Assisted Self Report for PTSD,* developed for GTZ during a vivo field mission in Somaliland, February-March 2002.

Wagenaar, W. A. & Groeneweg, J. (1990). The memory of concentration camp survivors. *Applied Cognitive Psychology, 4,* 77–87.

Waldron, S. (1987). Blaming the refugees. *Refugee Issues, 3*(3).

Ware, J., Jr., Kosinski, M., & Keller, S. D. (1996). A 12-Item Short-Form Health Survey: Construction of scales and preliminary tests of reliability and validity. *Med Care, 34,* 220–233.

Weine, S. M., Becker, D. F., McGlashan, T. H., Laub, D., Lazrove, S., & Vojvoda, D. (1995). Psychiatric consequences of "ethnic cleansing": Clinical assessments and trauma testimonies of newly resettled Bosnian refugees. *American Journal of Psychiatry, 152,* 536–542.

Weine, S. M., Kulenovic, A. D., Pavkovic, I., & Gibbons, R. (1998). Testimony psychotherapy in Bosnian refugees: A pilot study. *American Journal of Psychiatry, 155,* 1720–1726.

Weine, S. M., Vojvoda, D., Becker, D. F., McGlashan, T. H., Hodzic, E., Laub, D., Hyman, L., Sawyer, M., & Lazrove, S. (1998). PTSD symptoms in Bosnian refugees 1 year after resettlement in the United States. *American Journal of Psychiatry, 155,* 562–564.

Weine, S., & Laub, D. (1995). Narrative constructions of historical realities in testimony with Bosnian survivors of "ethnic cleansing." *Psychiatry, 58,* 246–260.

WHO. (1993). *International Classifications of Diseases* (Chapter Five). Geneva: World Health Organization.

WHO. (1997). *Composite International Diagnostic Interview (CIDI).* Geneva: World Health Organization.

WHO/UNHCR. (1996). *Mental health of refugees.* Geneva: World Health Organization.

Widom, C. S., & Morries, S. (1997). Accuracy of adult recollections of childhood victimization: Part I. Childhood sexual abuse. *Psychological Assessment, 9,* 34–46.

Widom, C. S., & Shepard, R. L. (1996). Accuracy of adult recollections of childhood victimization: Part I. Childhood physical abuse. *Psychological Assessment, 8,* 412–421.

Williams L. M. & Banyard V. L. (1999). *Trauma and memory,* Newbury Park, CA: Sage Publications.

Yehuda, R., & McFarlane, A. C. (1995). Conflict between current knowledge about posttraumatic stress disorder and its original conceptual basis. *American Journal of Psychiatry, 152,* 1705–1713.

Yule, W. (2001). Posttraumatic stress disorder in the general population and in children. *Journal of Clinical Psychiatry, 62* (Suppl. 17), 23–8.

*Anna B. Baranowsky, J. Eric Gentry, D. Franklin Schultz*

# Trauma Practice
## Tools for Stabilization and Recovery

Written to help guide clinicians through the maze of trauma treatment, this practical manual is effectively a structured toolkit of techniques and protocols to assist therapists in their challenging work with trauma survivors. With an emphasis upon cognitive-behavioral interventions, it provides resources and guidance for any psychotherapist working with any client. The manual is divided into three main sections, corresponding to Herman's (1992) Triphasic Model: Safety and Stabilization, Remembrance and Mourning, and Reconnection. For each of the three phases, it presents an array of techniques, protocols, and interventions, described clearly, thoroughly, and in a structured, easy-to-follow manner, in the four categories of cognitive, behavioral, body-oriented, and emotional/relational. This book promises to become an essential resource in trauma practice.

**Trauma Practice**
Tools for Stabilization and Recovery

Anna B. Baranowsky
J. Eric Gentry
D. Franklin Schultz

Hogrefe

A comprehensive, step-by-step guidebook, and an essential resource for all those treating trauma survivors.

**From the Reviews:**
*"...an excellent resource for trainers, teachers, and educators of trauma practitioners."*
       Charles R. Figley, PhD, Florida State University Traumatology Institute, Tallahassee, FL
*"Built on a strong empirically based foundation, this book is a must read for all therapists working with survivors of traumatic events."*
       Mark D. Lerner, PhD, President, American Academy of Experts in Traumatic Stress
*"This is how to present a 'how to' guidebook. It is more than an overview. It is a comprehensive step-by-step description of tools for the practitioner [...] Readers will be grateful for the help available in this book, which can be immediately used in the clinical setting."*
Louis W. Tinnin, MD, Founder and Medical Director of the Trauma Recovery Institute, Morgantown, WV

2005, 104 pages
softcover
0-88937-289-6
US $ / € 29.95

## Table of Contents

Acknowledgments • **About the Authors** • **Introduction: Trauma Practice: Tools for Stabilization and Recovery** • Purpose of this Book • Self-of-the-Therapist • Core Objectives • Book Description • Supportive Texts and other Recommended Readings • **Section 1: Foundations of the Trauma Practice Model** • Behavioral Therapy • Cognitive Therapy • Cognitive Behavioral Therapy • Cognitive Behavioral Therapy Research • Psychophysiology of Trauma • Tri-Phasic Model (Herman, 1992) • Necessary Ingredients for Trauma Recovery • Body, Cognition, Behavior and Emotion/Relation • Post-Trauma Response • **Section 2: Safety and Stabilization** • What is Safety? • Body • Cognition • Behavior • Emotion/Relation • **Section 3: Remembrance and Mourning** • Body • Cognition • Behavior • Emotion/Relation • **Section 4: Reconnection** • Body • Cognition • Behavior • Emotion/Relation • **In Closing** • **Afterword: Compassion Fatigue: The Crucible of Transformation** • Introduction • Compassion Fatigue: The Crucible of Transformation • **References** • **Appendix: Training Opportunities**

# Crisis

## The Journal of Crisis Intervention and Suicide Prevention

*Editors-in Chief: J F Connolly, Annette L. Beautrais*

### Aims and Scope

This well established periodical, now in its 26th year, publishes the most important articles on crisis intervention and suicidology from around the world. And Crisis is extensively cited in widely available abstracting services such as Index Medicus, PsycInfo, and Medline. But over and above this, the journal also includes potentially life-saving practical information for all those involved in crisis intervention and suicide prevention:

- Case studies from crisis intervention centers or from disaster and emergency services in the unique "Clinical Insights" section
- Regular columns in each issue written by some of the world's leading authorities, covering areas such as the management of crisis centers, school crisis counseling, emergency psychiatry, and jail or prison suicide
- Short reports, with brief summaries of particularly new and interesting studies
- Conference reports on the latest meetings around the world, as well as a calendar of forthcoming events and reviews of books, films, videos, information systems, training programs, and other intervention-related material

Crisis does not shy away from controversy: All sides of important current debates, such as the ongoing controversies about assisted suicide and euthanasia, have an opportunity to air their views, and letters to the editor frequently raise interesting questions about recent results or policy decisions.

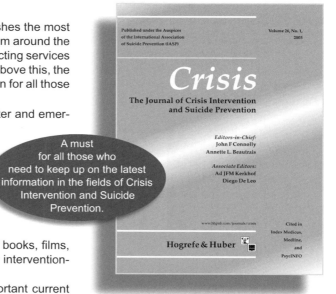

A must for all those who need to keep up on the latest information in the fields of Crisis Intervention and Suicide Prevention.

Subscription rates per volume:
Individuals: US $ / € 64.00
Institutions: US $ / € 96.00
Special rates for for members of
AAS - CASP/CPS: US $ / € 54.00
+ postage & handling US $ / € 12.00
ISSN 0227-5910

- Online access to the full-text of current and past issues (1999 – present) at www.psyjournals.com now included in subscription price
- Now in its 26th volume
- 4 issues per year
- Cited in Index Medicus, Medline, and PsycINFO
- Prestigious international editorial board
- Published under the auspices of the International Association of Suicide Prevention (IASP)

A Hogrefe Journal

---

## Order online at www.hhpub.com    E-mail: hh@hhpub.com    Order Form

**Hogrefe & Huber Publishers**
875 Massachusetts Ave., 7th Fl.
Cambridge, MA 02139, USA
Phone: (866) 823-4726
Fax: (617) 354-6875

**Hogrefe & Huber Publishers**
Rohnsweg 25
D-37085 Göttingen, Germany
Phone: +49 551 49609-0
Fax: +49 551 49609-88

Please quote "NET2005" when ordering

❏ **Please send me a free sample copy**

| Order date: | US $ / € | Qty | Total |
|---|---|---|---|
| Crisis – Individuals | 64.00 | | |
| Crisis– Institutions | 96.00 | | |
| | | | |
| | | | |
| | | | |
| | **Subtotal** | | |
| WA residents add 8.8% sales tax; Canadians 7% GST | | | |
| Shipping & handling US $ / € 12.00 per subscription | | | |
| | **Total** | | |

[ ] Check enclosed            [ ] Please bill me
[ ] Charge my:  [ ] VISA  [ ] MC  [ ] AmEx
Card # _____
CVV2/CVC2/CID # _____
Exp date _____
Signature _____
Shipping address (please include phone & fax):
_____
_____
_____